BELIEVE IT
ACHIEVE IT

BEND

BEATING THE ODDS AND COMING OUT ON TOP

DON'T

AFTER BATTLING CANCER TWICE

BREAK

REBECCA HERTZOG BURNS

I would like to dedicate this book to my caretaker, my mother. If it wasn't for her pushing me each and every day, watching over me, and studying up on what medications the nurses and doctors were giving me, I would not be here today. I am blessed to have such a loving mother who put her life on hold to be by my side 24/7.

I would also like to dedicate it to my family, friends, and the medical staff. I would not be so strong without their guidance and positive messages.

REFLECTING
BACK

LET ME START OUT BY TELLING YOU A little bit about myself. I am the baby of the family. I have an older sister and two older brothers. We are all very close in age; my sister is only six years older than me. I was a very active girl growing up, always involved in sports or physical activity. My sister was a cheerleader and a dancer, and I wanted to be just like her. My brothers, however, chose a different path for me. They told me I had to do sports, and I was on board with their plan.

When I went off to college, I decided I wanted to be my own coach. I loved to work out; I still do. It was my number one hobby. At the beginning of my sophomore year of college, I became involved in intermural sports. I was working out daily. I was out of the dorms and living in a cute little house with two of my best friends.

That September, I remember telling my mom how I
was having really bad night sweats—to the point that I
had to change my clothes in the middle of the night and
sometimes take a shower. We came to the conclusion that
it was probably just my new sheets, or maybe it was because
of the lotion I used after I took a shower each night. As
the weeks went on, I began to feel really weak. I remember
doing sprints at our university rec center and feeling as
if I was going to pass out. I didn't understand why I was
feeling so weak when I should have been feeling stronger.
In weight training, I noticed that instead of moving up in
weights, I had to use lighter weights.

One night, I came home from the gym and my roommate
said she thought my cat had flees. I literally ran to the store
to buy feline bath wash. (I was crazy like that!) It was a
little over a mile and I thought I could get more cardio in
that way.

That night, I gave my cat a bath. The next morning, I woke
up at 6:00 AM itching like crazy. I felt my side wondering
what was going on. I jumped out of bed and flipped my
lights on. My body was covered in a red rash in the shape
of a U. It started under my right breast, went all way
down my side, and up my back. It also followed along my
underwear line.

I immediately called my brother, Todd. I had been with him the weekend before and I thought maybe we had gotten into some poison ivy. We were both very allergic to it. Todd said he didn't have a rash and told me I had better go to the health center and get a shot. I called my mom, too, and told her about the rash. It looked like either I was bitten by a million fleas or had a really bad case of poison ivy.

I went to the health center and they thought I had a strep rash. My mom didn't buy it. After two days of taking amoxicillin, the rash was getting worse. My roommate suggested I go to Urgent Care. They drew my blood thinking I had poison in my blood or maybe had an allergic reaction to something. They gave me a steroid shot and sent me on my way. By the end of the week my rash was gone.

The following Monday I received a phone call from Urgent Care asking me to do a follow up with my labs. They noticed that my white cell count was a little low. I did a follow up and my counts began to come up. The nurse suggested I come back in ten days, after all the medications I had been taking for the rash were out of my system, and have my blood tested again. When I went back, my white count had dropped.

The doctor called me into her office and told me I needed to see a hematologist. I had no clue what a hematologist was. She called my mom and they decided it would be best to find an office nearby that could see me right away. That same day I went in and got my labs drawn by the hematologist. I went once a week to have my blood tested. Each week my count dropped. By week six, my hemoglobin and white count had dropped dramatically.

My parents drove down to Pittsburg, Kansas, where I was in school at Pittsburg State University, and we met with the doctor. A few days later I received my first bone marrow biopsy.

I remember it like it was yesterday. It still brings tears to my eyes thinking about that moment in time. I was sitting on my stability ball at the dinner table—remember, I loved to work out and this was just another way to work out while eating my dinner. I was expecting my roommate Tahnee to get home soon. Michelle was in the kitchen cooking her dinner. The front door opened, and my parents peeked their heads in. This was on a Wednesday night. I was surprised to see them.

"What are you doing here?" I asked, as if I didn't know the worst news ever was about to come out of their mouths. They came in and sat with me.

"Becca," they said, "you have cancer. You have Leukemia."

I couldn't believe it. I started yelling, "NO! NO! Why? Why me?" I couldn't understand it. I ate so healthily, and I worked out all the time! How could this happen to me?

I called my siblings and told them the news. My parents had wanted to tell me first. That night my whole family came together to be by my side. I remember calling my high school coach, too, to tell him about the diagnosis.

"Becca," he said, "Who made you strong?"

"My brothers did," I replied.

"Who holds all the records in the weight room at the high school?" he asked.

"I do." I said.

"This is going to be a boxing match. You're going to get your ass kicked a few times, but you have to keep fighting like hell, and you will come out with a victory."

After his pep talk, I went out into my living room, where my parents, siblings, their spouses, and some of my college friends were all sitting.

"Cry all you want to tonight," I said, "but after tonight, the tears end. I am going to kick cancer's ass. I do not want anyone to think negatively or ask me negative questions, I want this all to be positive. All I want from you guys is prayer and support."

We turned that night into a pizza party, dancing to Miley Cyrus's "Party in the USA."

I left school and started on treatment right away. I had good chromosomes, so my treatment was chemo only. My induction chemo put me into remission right away. That was followed by three rounds of consolidation chemo over a six-month period. On May 10, 2010 I was finished. My cancer was in remission!

IT CAME
BACK

IT WAS NEARLY FIVE YEARS SINCE MY
cancer had gone into remission—I was almost at the point
where I would be considered cancer-free. Life was amazing;
everything was falling into place. I went back to school and
graduated from the University of Mississippi, Ole Miss. I
met the love of my life, Tanner, in the spring of 2011. After
graduation, he got a job at the University of Arkansas as a
quality control football coach.

I moved there soon after he started his job and began
working at my dream job in the Athletics Department at
the University of Arkansas. It really was a dream come
true. College football coaches get the summers off, so I
took a week off during July and we went on a vacation.

The day I went back to work after our vacation was over, I woke up feeling really weird. I got out of the shower and told Tanner something wasn't right. I felt extremely weird. He assured me I was probably fine. But, of course, I called my mom anyway. She told me it was probably just the weather and the air pressure. I just really felt off, as if my hemoglobin was low. I put my shoes on and decided to go for a run. Then I would know if I was truly fine.

Later that morning, I went to work feeling so tired I could hardly keep my eyes open. I had to tough it out, since I'd only had my job for two months and had just gotten back from vacation. I thought that if I went home sick, they would think I was a pansy and not dedicated to work. Finally, about 11 AM, I told our HR person who sat behind me that I didn't feel very good. I ended up vomiting in the bathroom.

That was the first time I had gotten sick in ten years. Not even going through chemo made me sick. My coworker suggested I go to the campus health center. I went over my lunch break, assuming I'd go right back to work. I never returned to work that day.

The nurse drew my labs, due to my past experience with Leukemia. She also had me take a pregnancy test. Looking back, I wish that had been the case. The nurse walked into my room, her face ghostly white. She told me I needed to be admitted to the hospital right away. My white count was 0.9. The normal range is 4.8–12.

I called my cancer doctors in Kansas City. I remember texting Tanner that I had cancer again. He called me, frantic, and I explained everything to him.

Tanner offered to drive me home to Kansas City. I packed my bags like I would not be returning for a long time. Tanner was in denial. He thought the tests must have been just a fluke. I looked healthy, there was no way I had cancer.

That night, we stayed at my parents' house. My brother, Brian, and his fiancée, Katie, came down to spend the night with us. Brian and Tanner used to play football together when we were at Kansas State University.

The next morning, I was admitted into the University of Kansas Med Center to get a bone marrow biopsy. My parents, Tanner, all my siblings and their spouses, my grandparents, and my six best lifelong girlfriends were all there supporting me.

The biopsy was done that morning along with more labs. The team that came in to do my biopsy asked me if there were any medications that I wanted them to prep me with. I said no; I thought I'd be fine. I will never forget the biopsy technician. He kept saying my blood was clotting too much, they had to do the biopsy over again. I knew something was wrong. I tried to think positively and ignore what he was saying.

I held Tanner's hand throughout the procedure. He was trying not to watch, but he couldn't resist. After it was done, he said, "You might be the strongest girl I know. You just basically had an ice pick in your back, and it didn't even faze you."

The doctor told me he was keeping his fingers crossed, hoping that there was nothing to worry about. I was trying to keep positive and stay strong while I waited. I had the biggest room on the unit. My family and friends stayed with me until my results came back. We actually had to move to the lobby because there were so many of us. I also did a few laps around the unit while we waited for the results.

The hardest part of all this was having no control of what was going on with my body. The only thing I could control was my mind, so I prepared myself.

We were called back to my room around 2:00 PM. We walked right past my doctor, who was sitting at a desk waiting to come into my room. I remember seeing him there. He kept his head down as we passed. I had a bad feeling in my gut. As we all stood there in the room together, I heard the words I never thought I would hear again: "Becca, I'm sorry, your cancer is back."

This time, no tears came down my face. Not one. As I stood there, I looked around in the room and saw the fear in the eyes of my family and friends as they cried. I knew I could not be scared too, because that would scare them. I knew I could get through this. I knew that my family and friends and I could get through this. We had been there before. We had faced cancer before.

I was worried about Tanner and Katie. This was new for them. This time around I also had four nieces and nephews under the age of three who didn't understand. I walked around the room, hugging everyone and telling them it would be all right. I had beat it once, I could beat it again. I had no doubt.

"SCREW CANCER AGAIN," I said.

I asked my doctor if I could go outside one last time. Now that we knew I had cancer again, I wanted to begin treatment that night, and with treatment I knew I would be isolated for over a month. The doctor said yes and gave me twenty minutes to go outside before they hooked me up.

It was a beautiful day. Temperatures were in the 80s, it was sunny, and breezy. I never took deeper breaths than I did that afternoon. The slightest breeze never felt so good on my face. My siblings went home to get my nieces and nephews. That was the last time I would get to see them for a while: I wouldn't be allowed to be around anyone under the age of twelve.

We took family pictures together. I hugged my nieces and nephews tight and gave them a big kiss. It broke my heart saying good-bye to them. They were my world. I knew I had to fight for them so they could see their Aunt Becca again. I would have another opportunity to see them after I completed my induction chemo, but only if they were healthy.

That evening I got my PICC line put in and started on fluids and antibiotics. I would receive all my medications, IV fluids, and Chemotherapy through that PICC line. It was inserted in my arm with three lumens hanging down. A team came in and measured from my mid-bicep to my heart. They went in from the main artery in my arm to my heart. They placed a monitor on top of my heart and then watched the screen while they inserted the tubing. The tubing went from my arm all the way to my heart.

I was conscious the whole time they were doing this procedure and completely covered in what looked like a blue tarp. The people administrating the PICC line were fully gowned from head to toe, and no one else was allowed to be in the room. It's a very bloody procedure.

People often asked what my PICC line felt like. To be honest, it hurt when they numbed my arm to put the line in, but after that I couldn't really feel it, though my arm was very sore for a while after the initial procedure, depending on how much I moved. After a while I got so used to it, it pretty much became part of me. Other than the three lumens hanging from me, I didn't notice it.

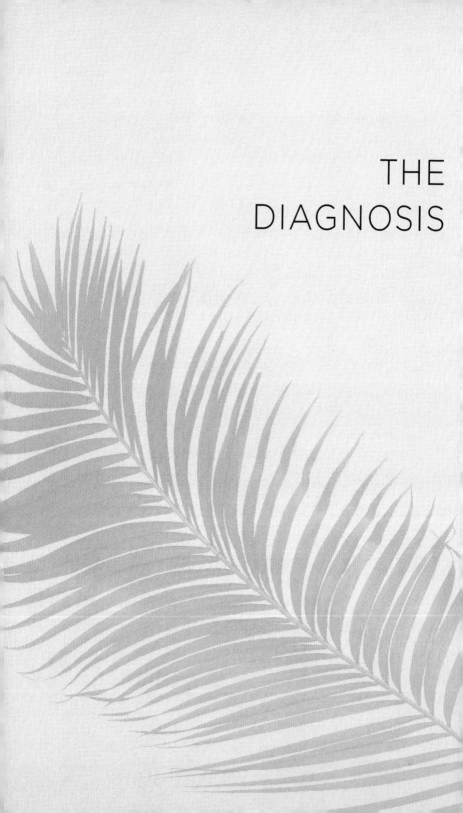

THE
DIAGNOSIS

I WAS ALMOST CONSIDERED CANCER
free. It takes five years of remission from Leukemia to be
considered cancer-free. At four years and ten months, I was
a relapse patient of Acute Myeloid Leukemia Inversion 16.
Normally, if you are to relapse, it will be within the first
year or two.

The cancer that I was diagnosed with in 2009 was the
same cancer that I was diagnosed with in 2014. My doctor
said there must have been a cancer cell hiding in my body
and it came back. When it returned, it came back with
the intent to destroy me. We were dealing with a serious
monster. My only treatment option was to put me into
remission right away with chemotherapy, followed by more
chemo and radiation, then a bone marrow transplant. I was
about to begin the fight of my life.

HAND IN
MARRIAGE

I HAVE NEVER BEEN SO PISSED AS I WAS
when I heard the diagnosis. I just did not understand the
timing. I believe things happen for a reason, but this time
I did not get it. Life was just getting started for Tanner
and me. We had our dream jobs and were just moving in
together.

The week we went on our trip, Tanner also asked my dad
for my hand in marriage. He was going to propose to me
the following weekend. I didn't know he asked for my hand
in marriage, but I did have a feeling that he was going to
propose soon.

After I found out I had cancer, I told Tanner, "You're not
allowed to propose to me till I am healthy and out of the

hospital." I felt so guilty that I ruined his plans and got sick at the worst time.

Luckily, everything started in July, when Tanner had time off work. He got to spend a lot of that time with me before he had to report back for Fall Ball. We were lucky that Arkansas was just a few hours down the road from the hospital.

Unfortunately, when Tanner did go back to work, he would not be able to be with me every day. I was only going to be able to see him when his team had a week off of playing and after football season was over. This journey was going to be the biggest test of our lives. If we could make it through this, we knew we could make it through anything.

NEXT
STEPS

I BEGAN CHEMOTHERAPY THAT
following morning, on July 16, 2014. This was the
induction phase. They needed to get me into remission
right away. That was the only option. I called the chemo
Super Woman Juice. I wanted to trick my mind and not
look at it as poison entering my body. I tried to make the
best of it and act like it was going to give me powers. Super
Woman Juice ran around the clock for the next seven days.
Each bag of chemo lasted a full day.

On top of that, I received additional chemo administered
through my PICC line for the first three days. A
chemo-certified nurse administered it over a fifteen-minute
period. It was a red chemo in a big syringe. I pretended it
was Kool Aid to trick my mind. I couldn't feel it going in

unless it was cold or if it went in too fast. Then I could feel it through my PICC line.

After my drip-chemo ended, the nurses would come in to hang the next bag of chemo. It finished at random times: 9 AM, 2 AM, even midnight. But no matter what time it was, as soon as the nurses came and changed my bag, I would get up and walk a mile around the unit: eight laps equaled a mile. The unit was a big square and that was all I saw for a month. Whenever I received a new bag, I felt that walking would help it pump through my veins.

My IV poll became my new best friend. I had to take it everywhere with me. I had to take it to the shower, on walks, to bed; you name it and it came along. My tubing was long enough so I could still feel somewhat free from the poll. When I took showers, they would wrap my arm in *press and seal*, like what you wrap your food with, then I would tape the top and bottom of it so no water would get into the PICC line site. I became a pro at wrapping my own arm!

While I was going through induction-phase chemotherapy, my doctors put me into the bone marrow registry list to start looking for a donor. We already knew that none of my siblings matched me. In 2009, they ran genetic testing on my sister and brothers. It very rare to have three siblings and not have a single match. We all had the same chromosomes, but they were in a different order. A donor had to be a perfect ten match. My oldest brother, Todd, was the closest match. He is what they called a half match: five out of ten chromosomes in a row matched. The doctors kept telling me that this situation is very rare. Little did I know being "rare" was going to stick with me throughout my cancer journey. I was always in the category of things that happen only in 1% to 5% of people.

I had to dig down and not let that get to me. I wasn't going to let cancer win: not now, not ever! I had too much to live for. So many great things were just about to take place. I never wanted to beat something so bad. Being involved in sports growing up gave me that competitive mindset to never give up, never quit, never stop believing, and always keep my faith.

This was my one shot, my one chance to look this cancer in the eye and take it down. I set goals to fight for not only myself, but for my family, Tanner, my friends, my job, and even my new car that I had only gotten to drive for a week. I had so much to look forward to. I knew I had to get healthy.

PALM
TREE

EVERY SUNDAY I WOULD WATCH JOEL
Osteen. His messages were powerful and always inspiring.
There was one that stuck out to me. He said that palm
trees are the strongest trees in nature. They can go through
storms, bending in the wind, but still stand tall afterwards.

That is how I envisioned myself: I was the palm tree. I
was about to go through the strongest storm of my life. I
was going to be beaten down, touch the ground, but after
the storm I was going to stand tall again. There was no
option. I might lose a few branches along the way, I might
be whipped around, but I was determined to stand up tall
again.

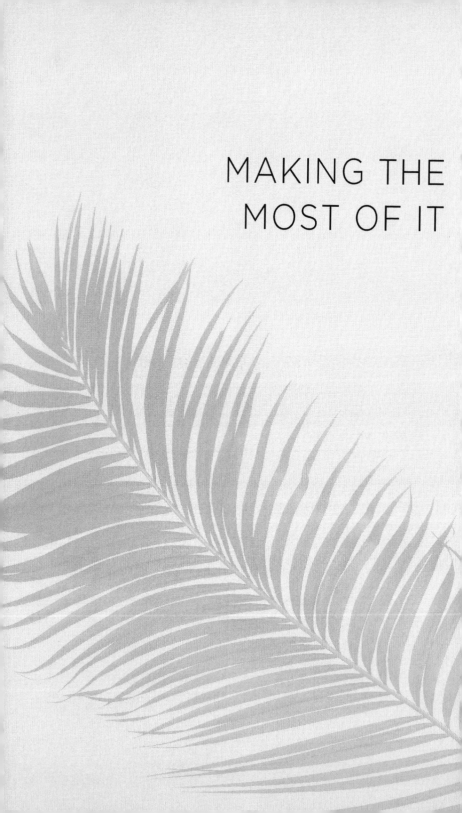

MAKING THE
MOST OF IT

OVER THE NEXT MONTH, I WOULD BE isolated. My counts began to drop dramatically. I would not be able to touch anyone after I went into isolation. I took precautions very early. Once I started chemo, I taped off my floor with blue painters' tape. I taped off the areas that were only for me. I had a designated chair that was only for me. I even had a sink and bathroom in my room that were only for my use. We called it "Becca's Area Only."

Every day, numerous times a day, I would wipe down everything with these intense wipes that were provided in the hospital. They were so strong, I had to wear gloves when I used them.

My friend, Theresa, came up with the idea to take a picture with every visitor who came to see me and hold up, with our fingers, what day it was. She would print the pictures that day, put it on a scrapbook page, and hang it up on the walls around my hospital room.

The doctors and nurses loved coming into my room. They said it was so uplifting to see all the support from my loved ones. It also was a constant reminder to me of how many people were helping me fight this fight. I knew I was not alone. We decorated my hospital room as if it was my own room. It looked like a freshman girl's dorm room: lots of color and lots of photos. I put every card I received up on the wall. We made the most of it. I had the mindset that I was going to win so I wanted to have good memories to look back on.

I completed my seven days of chemo. My doctors informed me that no one in the bone marrow registry list was a match. This was another occasion of being rare.

My sister got in touch with the Be the Match Foundation about hosting several bone marrow registry events. We were hoping that maybe we could find a donor match at the last minute. People from Arkansas, Kansas, Texas, and Missouri hosted drives help find a match for me. However, we were running out of time. The only way I would survive was to find a perfect donor, quickly.

On day fourteen my hair began to fall out. This is normally the hardest part for people, because you feel like you've lost your identity. That was not the case for me. It did not affect me one bit. I remember getting out of the shower one day. My friend Theresa was there with me. I was brushing my hair and it literally would not stop falling out. We laughed until we cried. I paged the nurse to get a comb thinking maybe that would help. The aide walked in and asked if we were ok, because we were laughing SO hard! I was hunched over trying to breath. I stood up and tried to act calm, asking if I could have a comb. He walked out and we began to laugh again.

That was the last time I would wash my hair. The next day we had a cutting party. My brothers and sister and their spouses took turns cutting my hair. Phase one: bangs. Phase two: mullet. Phase three: bowl cut. Phase four: mohawk. Phase five: spraying the mohawk red. Phase six: shaving it all off.

It was all over in a few hours. We had a good time with it. That day, Tanner was able to make it back up to see me. He was not there for the hair cutting party, but he did get to do the final shave. He said he knew he had a good-looking girl when she looked just as good, if not better, bald. He always says the right thing at the right time.

Because I still had a little hair left, I was not shiny bald. Over the next week my new hairbrush was a lint roller.

It was always so nice having Tanner with me for the weekend. He was on camp-out duty with me. I never spent a day or night without someone with me in my room. Nothing beat Tanner. We always had a blast together. He was my best friend; he knew me so well. We had been dating for six years by this point. We got to know each other on a whole new level. I did things in front of him I had never done before—like gas, for example. That's no joke with chemo, it was a big side-effect for me!

Tanner and I had to build our relationship on communication only—zero affection. It was always so hard saying good-bye to him. I knew it would be a while till I would see him again. All I wanted to do was give him the biggest kiss and hug, but that was all taken away from me. Because I didn't have an immune system, I was not allowed to touch other people.

I remember asking my nurses if I could give him a hug before he left one Sunday. They told us we could hug if we both gowned up and wore gloves and a mask. I never wanted to let go of him. I squeezed him so tight, really soaking it all in. I can still remember that hug today; it was a moment I will never forget. Affection is so strong, and we could not express that.

DONOR
DECISION

DAY TWENTY OF BEING IN THE HOSPITAL:

At this time, I was at the *nadir* stage waiting for my blood counts to start to recover on their own. During the nadir stage I had to avoid any possible source of infection. On day fifteen, they did a bone marrow biopsy, and they would do one again at day twenty-eight to make sure that the leukemia was dead.

Still, I kept waiting. No one had matched me yet for a bone marrow transplant. The only other option, the last resort, was to find a match from cord blood. Cord blood comes from the umbilical cord of a healthy baby. When the umbilical cord is cut from the child to the mother, that blood is removed and stored. This is free if the mother and father donate it. However, parents will sometimes pay to freeze it in case anything ever happens to the child.

My doctor came to my room to talk with me about my transplant options. "Rebecca, because you are healthy, you qualify for three study treatment options."

Yes "study." There is no sure answer on treatment options for Leukemia. It's all test studies, unlike other cancers that have exact treatments.

My doctor laid out my three options: a cord blood hyperbaric chamber, a Haplo, in which my brother Todd, who is my half match, would donate his marrow, or be put into a computer pool and allow it to choose which one I would do.

He gave me a few days to decide which option I wanted. I got to choose. Not my doctors. ME. That was the hardest decision I had to make. What if I chose the wrong one? What if the other option was a better choice? I asked all my nurses and family for their opinions. I'm the worst at making decisions on my own and I felt a lot of pressure. I was given packets about each option to read over and study. I gave one to each of my siblings, my parents, and Tanner. Each time I asked for their opinion, they would say, "Becca, it's your choice."

The decision weighed heavily on my heart. I knew for sure that I was not going to let a computer pool make my decision, so option three was out. It was between the Haplo treatment and the cord blood hyperbaric chamber.

I knew that the Haplo was a new treatment at my hospital. It hadn't been around when I was treated in 2009. My brother Todd and I look so much alike, compared to my other siblings. Our smiles are literally identical. Mom said our tempers were just alike, too. Her nickname for me when I was growing up was TJ: Todd Junior. Was that a sign that the Haplo was the right decision?

When I was in high school, I played softball over the summer. My coach was diagnosed with leukemia shortly after my own diagnosis in 2009. It ended up taking his life. When I went to see him before he passed away, he said, "Rebecca, I never want you to go through this again. I promise you that I will watch over you and make sure that you never get this disease again."

The day I found out that my cancer returned I prayed to my coach, Bob Dempski. I said, "Coach, please watch over me and be with me through this hard time. I need your help. You said you were going to watch over me to make sure I do not have to go through this again."

When my doctor told me about the cord blood hyperbaric chamber study, my mom asked about this study in relation to Coach's case. He said if it wasn't for Coach Bob Dempski, I would not be able to do this study: his foundation had funded these studies. Bob held a very special place in his heart, he said. When I learned that Coach Dempski's foundation had helped fund the cord blood hyperbaric chamber, I felt like that was God's answer to my prayer. I felt like that was Bob reaching out to me, letting me know he's going to be watching over me.

In the end, I followed my heart. I felt like God was answering my prayers, so I chose the option that was funded by my high school coach: the cord blood hyperbaric chamber.

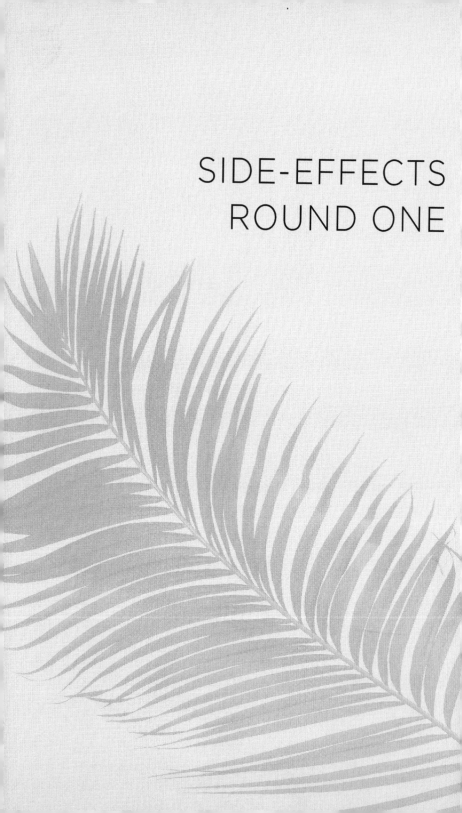

SIDE-EFFECTS
ROUND ONE

THE INDUCTION ROUND OF CHEMO GAVE

me crazy side-effects. I went into it with a small sore on my bottom lip, by the end of it I had three large sores in my mouth: on my tongue, under my tongue, and on the inside of my bottom lip. It was hard to eat, talk, and smile, but I continued to do all three. Before I ate, I would cover the sore on my bottom lip with KanKa. That stuff was magic! It kept me from feeling my teeth rubbing against my lip.

I asked my doctors if the sores would heal before I went in for a transplant. They assured me that as soon as my counts came up, the sores would go away. The sore on my bottom lip was the size of a dime and I still have the scar today.

During this time, I lost my sense of taste. In order for me to enjoy food, I needed it to be really spicy in order for me to taste any flavor. Nothing ever sounded good. I was placed on the neutropenic diet throughout my treatment. I was not allowed to have food from the outside. If I did, my mom had to prepare it. They were strict on the temperature of the food, how it was prepared, and how it was stored.

During induction chemo, I just stuck with the hospital food. My mom, or whoever was with me, would place the order. Since I never knew what I wanted, I would order a lot of food. I was also trying to gain weight before the transplant. The kitchen would always ask: "Is this all just for Rebecca?" After a few weeks they realized I could eat a lot.

When I was first admitted, I weighed 125. My weight jumped up from all the fluids I was taking in, but once I started the chemo it came off quickly. After that, I could literally eat anything and never gain a pound. I just kept losing weight. When I left the hospital in August 2014, before my transplant, I weighed 119. It was my goal to get my weight back up to at least 123 before the transplant.

I also experienced a lot of incontinence with induction chemo. That was not enjoyable. I ended up coming down with C-Diff, an infection of the colon. The only way to treat this is through antibiotics. They started me on that right away. This kind of infection is common for someone who has no immune system.

The nadir stage was the worst. This is the most common side-effect of chemo. My blood counts went to an all-time low and I ended up spiking a fever. I was put on an IV antibiotic. They had to remove the PICC line and wait 48 hours to replace it. At that time, all the medicines I was on went through an essential line.

One night I got up to go to the restroom and rinse my mouth out with my magic mouth wash: lidocaine. It would numb my whole mouth. I remember standing at the sink and I tilting my head back to get the lidocaine to the back of my throat. I spit it out, and boom! I began to black out. I yelled to my mom who was sitting on the couch. I don't know how she did it, but she ninja jumped across the room and caught me as I began to fall over. She quickly set me on the bed and paged the nurse.

I was tingling all over. My skin became clammy and I started to shake. The nurses came running. They were not sure why this was happening, and the doctors became concerned. They decided to do a spinal tap once I was released from the hospital before the transplant. They were afraid there might be cancer cells living in the spinal fluid.

They wanted to be able to cross all the possibilities off the list. Thankfully, that never happened again.

No matter how I felt, I never let it get me down. I got up every morning, showered, and got dressed for the day. I didn't dress like a slob. My mom told me on day one: you dress how you feel. If you dress like a bum, you're going to feel that way. You need to dress for success. Dress like you're going to work with your friends, and I did. I put my make up on every single day and I wore the cutest outfits I had. I never wore a hospital gown unless I was required to wear one for a procedure.

WAITING FOR
MY COUNTS

AFTER HITTING THE LOWEST POINT AND

my counts bottoming out, they slowly began to recover. Every night, the night nurses would draw my labs between 1 AM and 3 AM, depending on their rotations. They would check my vitals and weigh me, too. Talk about never sleeping! In the morning, the nurse would bring me my lab results. It was such a roller coaster ride!

I remember my doctor coming into the room one morning and asking me how I was doing. I told him my heart was beating fast; I was anxious about my counts coming up.

He said, "Your counts are beautiful and exactly where I want them." He told me he didn't expect them to recover for another week. Then he pointed at a picture of me on my wall and said, "That girl doesn't look anxious or worried about anything. That's the girl I want to see!"

That really perked me up!

As I waited for my counts to recover, I kept reminding myself that God was answering our prayers day by day. The power of prayer is AMAZING. I knew the good Lord was healing me. I was a palm tree going through a hurricane. God was lifting me up, getting me ready for the next storm I would be facing in the weeks ahead. Nothing would slow me down or break me, especially with the army I had behind me and God guiding me through the storm!

It took 31 days for my counts to recover enough for me to be released.

I will never forget my last night in the hospital. My dad stayed with me that night. The night nurse walked in. She was a different nurse than the one I was supposed to have. I always had the same nurses.

She came in and said, "Hi I will be your nurse tonight, I am not a fan of this unit. I never work over here." She left but said she would be back to meet with me in a few minutes.

I looked at my dad and I said, "Oh great! This should be interesting. I bet she is a mean lady." I was not looking forward to having her as a nurse. I even thought about requesting a different nurse. At that point, I had been on the unit for a month and I knew all of the nurses really well and I had great relationships with them.

My dad told me just to wait. "Let's see what she is like," and we both chuckled.

Little did I know that that night nurse was a gift from God. She came back into the room. We started going over everything. My dad asked her if she was new here.

She looked at him and laughed, "Honey I have been here for 22 years. I am far from new!" She said she usually only worked in the transplant unit.

I told her all my fears about going in for a transplant. I didn't know what to expect. How it was going to feel? Would I survive? Did I make the right choice with the cord blood transplant? What was it going to be like? What should I expect?

She said, "I have seen it all and you're going to be just fine." She was one of the nurses who had been on that unit the longest, working with blood cancers. She told me I had made a great choice doing the cord blood transplant. They had a great success rate. She made me feel so good about the transplant. I was her last patient to visit that night. I think we talked until 1:00 AM.

That night, when I went to bed, I was so motivated that I couldn't wait to get started. She gave me so much confidence and my dad and I were fired up. I think we even went and walked a mile that night around the unit.

During my whole journey I started a blog where I would write each and everyday. This is where I gained most of my strength to fight. I would love reading peoples comments on my blog. The comments would make me laugh, cry, and give me hope. Though out my book I share my blog post they are raw and what exactly was going on in my life at that specific time during my journey.

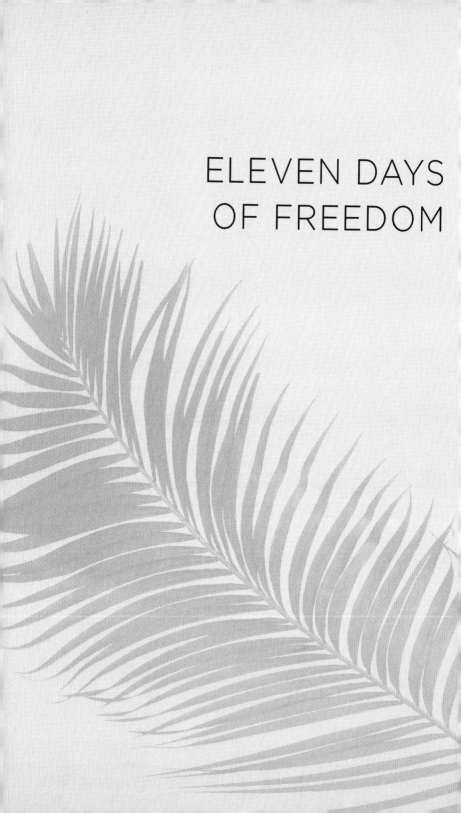

ELEVEN DAYS
OF FREEDOM

JOURNAL ENTRY

Good evening,

Today I learned a lot at my appointment at the Cancer Center! I have a full itinerary up until my transplant. Here is what will happen: on Tuesday I'll be getting a bone marrow biopsy to make sure my new cells are in remission. At the same time, I'll get a lumbar puncture done to make sure there is nothing hiding in my spinal cord fluid. Over the next week, I'll be getting my PICC line pulled out and a port put in.

I'll be admitted back into the hospital on August 29. I will be doing the Hyperbaric Chamber Cord Blood Transplant. They have two matches for me. They are both 5/6. One is a boy with O+ blood and

3.3 cell. The other is a girl with AB-blood and a 2.2 cell. Dr. Al will make the choice about which is better for me. He's the brains behind it all.

With that said, I'll be receiving the highest/strongest dosage of chemo and radiation. They want to wipe my marrow completely out. They told me it will make me feel weak, puny, give me really bad mouth sores, and a sour stomach. They said no matter how awful I feel, I have to get out of bed and move around. That's what is most important. I told them to BRING IT ON!!!

I have two weeks to get my mind right! I don't know if you know a Hertzog, but we're some crazy people. When given a challenge, I can't wait to beat it down and laugh at it like, "Ha, what challenge?" You don't stand a chance with me, cancer. I'm going to come out on top!!

I know this battle is going to be hard, but the best part about it is that I have the most amazing support group that's praying for me constantly!! I know I'll be able to best this because we are all going to start praying now. We want God to heal me and protect me.

I told Tanner I'll be kicking my season off the same time he's kicking off the Razorbacks' season. I'm going to go into this battle like it's football season. I'll get beaten down, pushed around, and tired, but I'll get right back up and keep FIGHTING! You better believe I'm going to come out with a VICTORY at the end of this season! I just got through preseason. I get two weeks to rest before GAME TIME!!

Please pray for my sore on my lip to heal over the next week, pray everything goes great with fertility and harvesting of my eggs, pray for me to be able to put weight on. Pray that the next round of chemo I start end of August won't give me bad mouth sores, upset stomach, or make me feel weak or puny. Pray for God to give me strength and motivation, and that He'll keep my lungs, heart, liver, kidneys all healthy through this battle. Most importantly pray for the victory that the good Lord is going to give me in the end!

BWB

Believe it. Achieve it.

Becca

MY LAST WEEK IN THE HOSPITAL, I MET with a fertility specialist to try and harvest my eggs before going into transplant. Tanner and I decided to freeze the embryos together, instead of just my eggs.

I started right away doing an IVF treatment. Technically, my cancer doctor only wanted me to have seven days off. He was stretching it to give me eleven days. We needed as many days as we could get. In order to get my eggs, they really needed a full month, but we absolutely could not wait that long. The longer you wait after induction chemo, the more likely your cancer could come back. Then it's even harder to get you back into remission again. We were working against the clock.

My eleven days out of the hospital before my transplant were far from free. I was still making daily visits to the cancer center. I was also getting every test under the moon done before going in for a transplant. I had a spinal tap, an EKG, a panel of my mouth, lab work after lab work, a pulmonary lung function test, a bone marrow biopsy, and more.

My first day home from the hospital, however, was amazing! My mom made me exactly what I requested for dinner: steak, shrimp, and my all-time favorite cheese potatoes. It was delicious! Earlier that day, when I got home, I didn't want to go inside. It was so beautiful outside. I got a lawn chair and sat under a big shade tree. It was so amazing to feel the breeze and sunshine. I was wearing my mask and a hat and not really in the sun of course, but I'm an outdoors girl! It's always been hard for me to stay inside. Any chance I have to be outside, I'm there.

My 25th birthday happened during my eleven days of freedom. All my girlfriends: Kali, Katie, Kelsie, Kuss, Theresa, and Michelle threw me a party. We all went to Kelsie's house. I felt like a normal person again. My friends never treated me like I was sick. We talked about everything except my health. They are all such amazing people and they never left my side during this battle.

All of them are either schoolteachers or work around lots of people every day. My doctors said that, because they work around children and young adults and because of flu season, it was best if they didn't come to visit me when I was in the hospital for my transplant. We expected that, so my birthday party would be the last time I would see them for a while.

After the party, I said "I'll see y'all in a few weeks!" I knew I was going to be just fine. Other than cancer, I had good health. Surely I would get through this with flying colors.

I also went to see all my nieces. Unfortunately, my nephews were sick at the time, so I was not able to see them. I gave my nieces the biggest hugs ever. They had fun rubbing my head. It was hard for them to understand what I was going through. My oldest niece was three. She kept telling me "Aunt Becca I am going to pray to God every night to heal you and keep you healthy. I know He will." Little kids always amaze me with what they say.

That was the last time I would see them until Christmas, about one hundred days after my transplant.

My dad purchased an RV, hoping I would be healed up enough to take me to a football game that fall to see Tanner. Every fall, before the season starts, there is a fall scrimmage. I made sure I did not have any appointments that day. My parents, our dog Bruiser, and I packed up the RV and headed south to Arkansas. Tanner didn't know I was coming down. I told him I had an appointment and wasn't going to be able to make it.

I was texting the Football Operations Manager, Mark, about it. I had it all planned out. I wanted to surprise Tanner on the football field. We arrived in Arkansas on a Friday night. I told Mark that I wanted Tanner to walk out onto the field and I would be there to surprise him.

But Mark said, "Let's go BIG! I will get you mic-ed up and record it."

So, we went big! After the team finished with practice that night, Mark told Tanner and the other guys that he needed them to go move equipment off the field. At that point,

I was standing on the 35-yard line with a microphone attached to me and the football video crew videotaping. Tanner walked out of the tunnel and saw me. That was our first time seeing each other in weeks.

His first words were, "What the hell?"

Then he came and gave me a huge hug and we all laughed. The other guys gave me a hug too and rubbed my head. That night we went back to the RV for a cookout with my parents. I was able to down a lot of food. I only weighed between 115 and 120 lbs. at this point. I wanted to get back to 125 before I went into transplant. I remember I had two cheeseburgers and a hot dog, plus mac and cheese. Never before have I been able to have that much food at once.

I spent the night with Tanner at our apartment. We were not allowed to have sex at all—my doctors stressed no sex until after the transplant was a success. We didn't even care about that. All I cared about was that I could hug him again and give him a kiss. That was more magical than anything else. I hadn't hugged or kissed him in more than a month and a half. Just being in his arms again meant the world to me. That night, laying in our bed, we cried and laughed together and talked about everything that was about to take place. We knew this was going to be our last time to sleep in the same bed together for a very long time. Once the transplant took place, I would have to go back to my bubble, not able to touch, hug, or kiss until I had a white count again.

As I laid there with Tanner, I remember thinking how unfair this was. We were just getting our lives started. Why did this happen now? Would we have to face challenges like this for the rest of our lives?

Tanner always made me smile. I knew he had to be hurting inside too, but he just didn't want me to know. He kept me in check. He made sure I didn't get "too soft on him," as he would say. We never talked about death or "what if . . ." We both remained very positive. Tanner was confident in me, and that gave me the confidence to beat cancer. Moments like that are what I fight for. I wanted to fight so that we could be there for each other for the next fifty years of our lives.

It was always bittersweet watching Tanner leave. He's an amazing guy to drive up as often as he did for me. As a coach, you don't get much time off. We had such great support from the Razorback coaching staff, giving him the opportunity to see me. I received 21 letters in the mail from the whole football coaching staff!

CARETAKER

IN THE BEGINNING OF MY ELEVEN DAYS
of freedom, I received a spinal tap. Of course, because I
was always the "rare case," I ended up getting a drip issue
where fluid goes to your brain. It only happens to one in
five people, and I was that one person. It felt as if someone
was sucking my brain out of me and trying to pull it to the
ground, but my body was forcing it upwards. It was a weird
feeling. I could not be upright; I had to be laying down or
reclining. My doctors said drinking soda would help, but
that did not help at all. I am not a pop drinker anyway, so
that did not sound too appealing. They told me that after
a week, it would go away—just in time for preparation
treatment before the transplant.

In order to be able to receive a transplant, we were required
to have a caretaker that could be there for me 24/7. My

mother was my caretaker. We had to attend a meeting
to learn about what was expected. There were nine of us
who attended the meeting with our caregivers. Both my
mom and my dad attended the meeting with me, as well
as my friend Therese, who would help out as much as
she could. During that meeting, I had to lay down on the
floor because of my spinal tap. That was the only way I felt
normal.

We received a large binder full of rules on what I was not
allowed to do and what the caretaker had to do. They had
to know all my medications, what time of day I took them,
and how I reacted to the medications. I was no longer
allowed to clean anything or make anything. Anything
that came into my room had to be wiped down with
disinfectant cloths. Everyone who entered my room would
be required to wash their hands. No outside food was
allowed in my room unless it was in a package. My mom
could not even leave to get lunch and come back in and eat
it in my room.

When we left the meeting, my mom said, "I'll have to care
for you 24/7."

I laughed and said "Oh yeah, right! You will not!"

Little did I know she would become more than just a caretaker for me. She was my mother, nurse, doctor, drill sergeant, housekeeper, and cheerleader. She had to do everything. If it wasn't for my mom, pushing me every day, I would not be here today. She kept my fighting spirit alive. I would get so pissed off at her and we would have screaming wars, but it was because I was so tired and just wanted to stay in bed. She would get pissed that I was not moving. She knew that if I didn't get out of bed, I would not make it through my battle.

MEETINGS,
MEETINGS,
AND MORE
MEETINGS

BEFORE GOING IN FOR THE TRANSPLANT,

I had to attend several meetings with the hematologist
and the radiologist. I remember it like it was yesterday.
My mom and I arrived at the radiation center that was
connected to the hospital. They took me into a room and
a sweet lady with an English accent measured my height,
weight, and all of my bones from my skull to my feet. She
said she needed to know how much lead to use on me when
receive the radiation. I would wear weights of led to cover
my lungs and liver. The radiation would kill them if they
did not protect them. They had to know how much led
I needed vs radiation. They also had me practice sitting
in the chair that I would be sitting in when receiving
radiation. The best way to describe it is an electric chair.
They strapped my head and arms down so they would not

move. After that, my mom and I met with the radiology specialist and a resident who was shadowing him.

The doctor went over all the side-effects I was going to face, both short-term and long-term. He said I would not be able to have children and that I could potentially develop another kind of cancer from doing this procedure. I told him I didn't need to hear any of his warnings. I told him I am an animal and I would kick cancer's ass. I knew I was going to be just fine. God would not put me through this again.

He went on to talk about my radiation schedule. I would get radiation twice a day, morning and evening, for one hour at a time, thirty minutes on each side, for four days straight. I would be given the strongest dosage possible. He said that during that time I would have to sit still.

I remember telling them that I needed a mirror to place in front of my face. They both looked confused. "A mirror?"

I said, "Yes, a mirror to look at myself and get myself PUMPED UP during radiation." I then gave him the "Hertzog Evil Eye" and said, "Don't you mess with me! You're messing with an ANIMAL!" Everyone in the room lost it. The resident was laughing so hard he was tearing up!

The doctor said, "Now I am worried! I have never dealt with an animal before."

JOURNAL ENTRY

Today I met with my radiologist oncologist. He was a younger doctor he. He had a resident following him. The resident was a guy about my age. He went over why I need this strong form of radiation, all the pros and cons of the radiation, and the side-effects. He told me if I handled chemo well, I should be able to handle this well too. He said the side-effects are nausea, mouth sores, and fatigue. I told him "you don't have to worry about the fatigue part, I'm mentally tough." He laughed.

My treatment will be for an hour, twice a day, for four days. I will be getting a total of eight rounds of radiation over a four-day period.

They measured my whole body, bones and all. This was so they know how much lead to pump into me. They showed me the room I was going to be getting treatment in. I will be sitting in a chair/bed with my knees bent and strapped in. They said my head will also be taped to the back so I can't move.

I asked the doctor if I was allowed to shake my feet and tap my fingers during radiation. I said it's hard for me sit still for five minutes. He said that was allowed. I also asked to my phone in to play music over my own Bluetooth speakers. He said that's allowed, too. Then said I was going to need a mirror. I held my hands up making a mirror in front of my face. I said I need a mirror right here. The doctor and resident both looked at me like, a mirror? I said that's for me to look at myself and get myself PUMPED UP during radiation.

They smiled. I gave them the Hertzog evil eye and said "You're messing with an ANIMAL!" They both started dying laughing. I think the resident had tears he was laughing so hard!

He said, "We will make that happen for you."

KICK-OFF

TODAY'S THE DAY: AUGUST 30TH, 2014. I
started the morning out at the fertility clinic to see if I had
any eggs to retrieve. Unfortunately, they were not able to
retrieve any eggs when I was put under for retrieval. I have
never cried so hard as when I found out I would never be
able to have a child of my own. It was even harder than
hearing the news that I had cancer.

My friends and family were so supportive. They told me
the most important thing was my health and my life. I
cried for two days. I could not wrap my head around the
thought of not being able to see my own creation. I knew
I had to refocus and put that dream behind me. God
had other things in store for me. There must have been
a reason why they couldn't retrieve my eggs. Maybe they
were damaged from all the chemo in my past. Maybe I

was supposed to adopt. Maybe God would bless me with a miracle baby. Somehow, some way, I knew I would have kids, but first I had a battle to fight and win.

My mom and Theresa were there with me when I came out of anesthesia. We got in the car and headed to the hospital. I was admitted first thing in the morning. I remember walking into the hospital with Theresa and my mom.

Theresa, also known as Tab, said "Bec, you better take it all in because your ass will be in here for a while!" we all started laughing.

I was decked out in my new Arkansas gear that the coaches' wives and girlfriends got for me at the beginning of football season. Tab took a picture of me outside of the hospital with my arms opened wide and a football in my right hand. I wore a razorback tank top, a new zip up jacket, leggings and new shoes. I was ready to whoop cancer's ass!

We walked into the front doors of the hospital, took the elevator up to the fourth floor, and walked over to unit 41, where I would spend the next few months. I had a great room. It was spacious and overlooked the garden. The unit was under construction, so half of it was completely blocked off. It was also a very strict unit. Visitors entered through three different sets of double doors and had to vigorously wash their hands for fifteen seconds and wipe down anything they were bringing in. They knew if people were following the rules or not, because everyone was monitored by camera 24/7. If they heard or saw someone cough, sneeze, sniffle, anything, they would ask a series of questions and often turn that person away. Visitors had to be as healthy as an ox to be allowed in.

I was only allowed two guests in my room at a time. Whenever I had several guests, they would take turns coming up to see me. The rules never changed throughout the treatment. Everyone who came to visit had to have had a flu shot and be sick-free for two weeks. If they had been around anyone who was sick, they could not come to see me for two weeks or more. I was truly isolated. We also made a rule that no one could touch me. That meant no hugs, high-fives, handshakes, or kisses. Absolutely no touching, no matter what.

That afternoon, I started my first bag of chemo for my transplant in ten days. I was excited to get started. That bag of Super Woman Juice, the chemo, only lasted about two hours and I didn't feel any side-effects right away.

The day I started chemo was also the same day Tanner kicked off football season. We were kicking off on the same day. It was fun watching the game that Saturday and cheering them on. I knew he was cheering me on too. I treated my illness as if it was football season. It was going to be long, hard, and a lot to fight for. I knew I would get beaten every now and then, but in the end, I was going to come out with a victory. Nothing was going to slow me down.

This is what my treatment schedule looked like over the ten-day countdown to transplant day:

Days 10–8: Chemo only. Each bag was an hour long.

Days 7–4: Full body radiation, twice a day for an hour each time, morning and night.

Days 3–2: Chemo again

Day 1: Rest day

Day 0: Transplant Day!

JOURNAL ENTRY

Day +10

My doctor told me I was in the best condition possible for starting this battle. My scans, my x-rays, and all my organs are in tip-top shape! This is another blessing God has given me before starting this next chapter. The headaches I was having were all related to the spinal tap that I had a couple weeks ago.

Sept. 9th is Hyperbaric Chamber and Transplant Day. I'll be placed in the chamber and I'll receive 100% oxygen for two hours. I will then go back to my room and rest for six hours. Then a nurse will come into my room and transfuse me with the umbilical cord blood transplant through my port over a period of thirty minutes. Then we will patiently wait for the cord blood to make itself at home in my marrow.

This is something that we all need to start praying for now. We need the cord blood to engraft! This means that the new cord blood will start working in my body as my new marrow. This process can take 14–30 days. The cord blood that I will be receiving is from a baby boy who is O+. This is the only information that I will ever receive about my donor. With receiving his cord blood, my blood type will switch from B+ to O+ and I will have his immunity. Which means I will have to get all of my childhood immunizations again.

PERSONAL
GOALS

BEFORE I STARTED TREATMENT, I MADE
several personal goals for myself after attending all the
meetings to learn about what was to come.

First, I decided I would not be put on a feeding tube. They
said that most patients have to be put on a feeding tube,
but it could cause a serious infection. I told them they
would not have to worry about me. I love food and I would
not allow them to put me on a feeding tube. I would do all
I could to eat.

My second goal was to walk to and from the radiation
unit every day. It was on the opposite side of the hospital,
round trip it was probably about a mile. I would walk this
every morning and afternoon with a hospital assistant who
would come to get me.

Next, I would get out of bed and shower every day. I would not lay in my bed unless I absolutely had too. I was determined that my bed was just for sleeping at night or for naps. Other than that, I did not need to be in there.

I also set a goal to exercise regularly. My unit was under construction, so I couldn't walk very far, other than up and down the hall. But, I could make several trips up and down the hall throughout each day. I would also do twenty squats at the end of each walk.

My last goal was to WIN. I was determined to kick cancer's ass. I was not ready to die. I had so much ahead of me. Tanner and I were just getting started with our lives. I didn't want my nieces and nephews to grow up not knowing their Aunt Becca. I had a brand-new car that I had only gotten to drive for a week! I could not wait to get healthy and get on with my life.

Mind over matter and keeping my faith in the good Lord was how I was going to get through this. I was fully confident in myself and what I could do. I also had a huge support team backing me, which gave me even more motivation. My doctors and nurses believed in me, too. All this gave me the confidence I needed going into the battle of my life.

JOURNAL ENTRY

Siblings

Good evening!

Today has been a fun day! My siblings and their spouses came up to visit me. Of course, they had to take turns visiting since I'm limited to only two people in my room at a time. We played board games and Wii. I also played Wii with my parents, and that was quite entertaining!

It's day -8, I finished my third round of Superwoman Juice around 3 PM. Tomorrow is the big day to start radiation. I will get premeds at 5 AM and I'll be transported to radiation at 6 AM. I have requested that they let me walk with the transporter tomorrow instead of being wheeled down. I figured I might as well get my walking in while I still feel good!

I have never experienced radiation, but I'm ready to take it on. My night nurse told me tonight the three things for success: eating, walking, and having a positive attitude. I believe the good Lord has blessed me with all three qualities.

Everyone I have talked to says that the number one side-effect of radiation is fatigue. I know I'll get fatigued, but I know the good Lord will give me the strength to fight through it and give me the ability to get up and walk my unit! I BELIEVE IT.

Over the next four days, I will receive radiation twice a day: once in the morning and once in the evening. This will be full-body radiation. This will be one of the hardest parts of my journey. I ask that we pray for my strength as I go through this part of my journey.

I love reading everyone's posts and what you write to me on Facebook, too. Just because I don't respond doesn't mean I do not read them. I read them each and every day. They are what give me the strength to beat this battle once and for all, for the rest of my life! This isn't just my battle; this is OUR BATTLE!! Please pray for my strength, my overall health, my body to continue to respond to the treatments, my appetite to stay great, and most importantly for my body to accept my new cord blood transplant that I will receive September 9th!

BWB

Believe it. Achieve it.

Becca

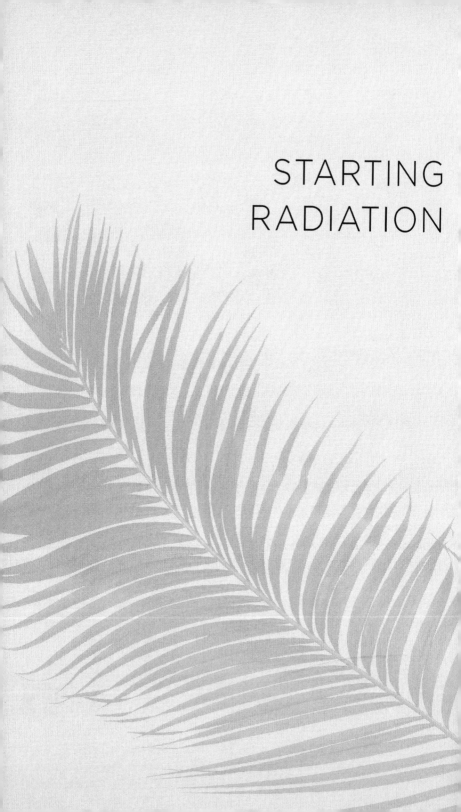

STARTING
RADIATION

AFTER FINISHING CHEMO, I STILL FELT

pretty good. I didn't have to worry about my hair falling out with the radiation because it still hadn't come back. The first morning, I was ready to go. I had my speaker hanging from my poll so I could listen to music during my treatment.

I remember the hospital aid who came to take me down to radiation showed up with a wheelchair and asked if I was ready. I said, "Yeah, I'm ready, but I am not getting in the wheelchair. My ass is walking there and back!"

He was shocked. He said, "No one has ever walked before."

I said, "Well I am."

He said "Ok, but I need to make sure your doctors are ok with it." The nurse paged the doctor, and sure enough, they were all ok with it.

Each day a different person took me down to radiation in the morning and in the afternoon. They all knew about me. They would say, "I've heard about you and how you actually walk. That's so awesome! I've never had anyone walk with me before."

The radiologist told me that once I finished all of the rounds of radiation, I got the honor of ringing the bell. I said, "Oh don't you worry, I will ring that bell as hard and as loud as I can!"

I was about a day into my radiation treatment. My nurse walked into my room and was going over everything with me. She said, "Oh, you're on radiation. Yikes! Girl, you're going to be miserable! Here in a few days, you will begin to vomit, have an awful sore throat, and really bad fatigue. You're going to lose your eyebrows and your lashes. It's going to be bad."

I was so pissed. I was thinking, "Lady do you know who I am? I don't need to hear that shit." When she left, I told my mom how pissed I was. My mom told me to just blow her off. Everyone is different. Little did I know, that nurse was exactly right.

It was day 6 when the side-effects starting kicking in. I was halfway done with radiation. I only had two more days left. That morning, when I woke up, I felt really nauseous. I was on the verge of throwing up. I hit my nurse call-button as soon as I felt it coming. When they came to check on me, I asked for Zofran, ASAP. Zofran was a medication that would help calm my nausea.

My bones were beginning to ache. There were new side-effects each day. My jaw hurt, making it hard to chew food. The radiation had damaged my salivary glands, causing me to have cotton mouth. The radiation really took a toll on my glands, esophagus, and stomach. They felt it the worst.

Day -4 finally arrived, and I was officially done with radiation! I rang the bell hanging on the wall and everyone came out and clapped for me. My radiation doctor walked me back to my room that evening. He said he wanted the honor of walking me back. I asked him how long the side-effects would last and what I should feel. He said feeling nauseous would end soon, but the fatigue would last until my counts started to recover after my transplant.

He said the worst side-effect was a raw throat. He asked me if my throat was sore. It wasn't. I was just tired and nauseous. He told me throat pain was usually the number one worst side-effect for patients. He said it often got so bad patients had to be put on pain meds. I told him, "Remember, your messing with an animal! I believe, with all our prayers, we can keep this from happening to me!"

He also told me I was one of the only inpatients that had walked to and from radiation. I was proud of myself. That was one goal completed.

A few days later, the nausea and fatigue were in full force. I was throwing up every morning right after I woke up. I finally put a large trashcan next to my bed that was the perfect height for me to lean over and throw up. I was tired all the time and I started napping a lot. The fatigue was from my nausea medication and the radiation. Even though I was very tired, I would still walk the unit and do squats. My mom made sure of that, so did my friend Theresa, who was there almost every single day, too.

My mother was a drill sergeant. She would tell me to get my ass out of bed, stop feeling sorry for myself, and go shower. I would tell her I was too tired. She would get so mad, but there wasn't a day I didn't take a shower. I had to be in there by 9:30 AM every morning. That was our deal. When I was in the shower, the aide would come and change out my bedding. This became a daily routine.

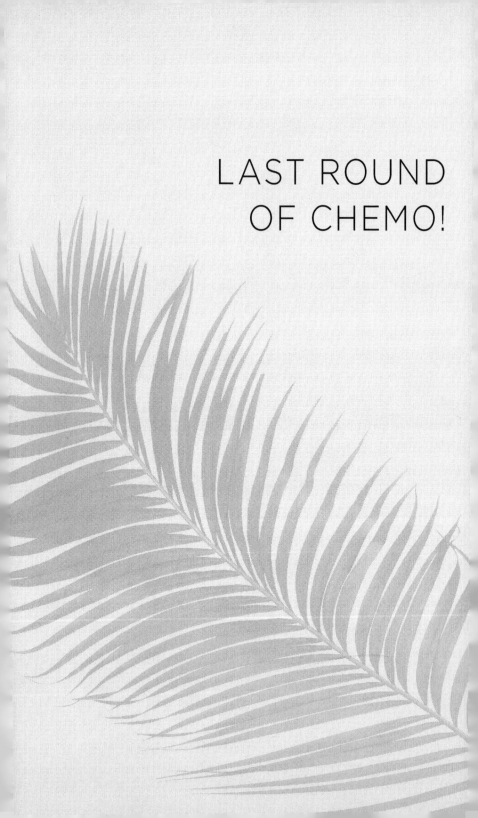

LAST ROUND
OF CHEMO!

IT WAS DAY -2. TIME FOR MY LAST
round of chemo EVER! I would never have to take chemo
again. The Superwoman Juice got the best of me the last
day. I was getting sick several times a day, and now my nose
was burning, too. You know how, when you're swimming,
you get a rush up your nose and it burns and makes
your eyes water? That is how I felt for two hours while I
received the Superwoman Juice.

After chemo, it was hard keeping food down. I had to
wait until my nausea subsided before I could eat. This
still didn't slow me down. I was focused on the next day's
adventures and kept thinking how it was only going to get
better!

JOURNAL ENTRY

Day Off

Good Evening!

Today is Day -1! Today has been a pretty relaxing day. I woke up this morning and got sick, but I'm feeling much better now. My throat is a little sore from the radiation, but hopefully it won't last long. Tomorrow is the BIG DAY!

Tomorrow will be Day 0 and a new birthday for me! I will go down to the burn unit between 8 AM and 9 AM to get into the hyperbaric oxygen chamber for two hours. I get to take a movie with me to watch for the duration of the treatment.

The chamber is part of a study that my doctor, Dr. Al, designed. Patients get in the chamber and receive pure oxygen over two hours. The pure oxygen is supposed to help the new cells find the marrow faster and decrease the chance of infection. He is doing this study to see if the pure oxygen will help shorten the amount of time it takes for my counts to recover.

Once I am out of the chamber, I will go back to my room and six hours later I will receive my cord blood. The cord blood will be in a giant syringe and my nurse will infuse it over a thirty-minute time period. It comes frozen, so during the six-hour break between the chamber and receiving the cord blood, it will thaw out in my room.

Once I receive my new cells, they will monitor my vitals. Increased blood pressure is a common side-effect of the transplant. We have been praying for this for a long time now, and it is finally here! The cells will find my marrow and live there. They will divide and grow and they will become my new cells. I will have a new blood type: O+. My previous blood type was B+; I used to "be positive" but tomorrow I'll be "ohhhh so positive."

Since tomorrow is the big day, we will all have our BWB shirts on so I hope you will too (old or new ones!).

I decided on a name for my new cells and it is . . . DRUMROLL PLEASE. . . .

Red Rock Palm Potion. This name is perfect because Red Rock is the name of the bull in one of my favorite movies, "8 Seconds." The palm potion fits because I have said from the beginning that God made me a palm tree, because they are much stronger after the storm. This storm will not knock me down, it will only make me that much stronger . . . with help from my Red Rock Palm Potion!

PLEASE, PLEASE, PLEASE pray for me that my throat soreness will subside, that my organs will stay healthy through all of this, that my nausea will go away, that my appetite and energy level will stay up, and most importantly that my body will accept my new cells and engraft as they should without any complications!

Please keep me in your thoughts and prayers tonight and tomorrow. I thank you all soooo much for the continued support. I will update you tomorrow after the transplant.

BWB

Believe it. Achieve it.

Becca

NEW CELL
DAY

SEPTEMBER 9, 2014 WAS THE DAY THAT I was getting my new cells. I was so excited. I was going to be born again! That morning, when I woke up, I got ready to head down to the hyperbaric chamber. The team that was overseeing my study was there to walk me through the day. After I ate breakfast, I headed down. My mom, dad, and the doctor I was doing the study under all walked me down to the burn victim area. That was where the hyperbaric chamber was located in the hospital.

I remember, when I got there, I had to pee so badly I thought I was going to wet my pants. This was an ongoing problem for me. I was pumped with so many fluids that I constantly had to go to the restroom.

After I went to the restroom, I got into the chamber. I posed for a picture with my doctor, holding two thumbs up. I was excited to be a part of this study and to get into the chamber. They had a selection of movies to watch. I chose Happy Gilmore. I was placed in the chamber for two full hours with no break. I had to lay on my back the whole time. There wasn't much room.

The chamber looked exactly like the tubes you put your money in at a bank, only human sized and with a pad to lay on. They gave me a pillow and a barf pan and locked me in. There was a lady sitting next to my chamber, to talk me through what I was going to be feeling until they got it to 100% oxygen. She told me my ears would start popping and I would feel pressure, which is exactly what happened. After we got past that pressure point, it stopped, and I did not notice anything different. It almost felt like I was on an airplane.

After she got me to 100% oxygen, she said I wouldn't be able to hear them, but they could hear me if I needed anything. There were two of us in the chambers: me and another guy who was a burn victim.

I was about 45 minutes in and I had to go pee again really bad. I asked if I could use the restroom. However, she said that if I got out, I would ruin the study and it wouldn't work. I was wondering if I should just pee my pants or pee in the barf pan. Instead, I held it. There was no way I was getting out and ruining the study. Of course, that made it hard to relax while I was in there. When my two hours were up, they slowly brought the oxygen back down. I sprinted to the restroom with my poll. It was painful holding it for so long while I was getting pumped with fluids!

My parents met me outside the restroom and we walked back to my room. I was able to take a nap and rest until I received my transplant.

Later that day, my nurse and the aide decorated my door, top to bottom, with a palm tree. It was so pretty and awesome. Needless to say, I was spoiled by the nurses. Everyone else on the unit just had a small sheet of paper on their door that said, "New Cell Day," and gave the date. We had to keep our room doors closed due germs. They made my door look a giant palm tree because my symbol through all of this was a palm tree, and because I had named my cord blood Red Rock Palm Potion.

All my siblings and their spouses were there that afternoon. Theresa was also there. She brought me an extremely large birthday hat and beads to celebrate, since this was the day I was going to be born again, my new birthday: September 9, 2014. We all had our *Believe it. Achieve it.* shirts on. *Believe it. Achieve it.* was and always will be my moto, ever since 2009. I took pictures with everyone in front of my bedroom door before I received my transplant.

When I was in the chamber, and the whole afternoon while I was relaxing, my new cells were thawing with a specialist watching over them. My dad asked how many cells I would be getting. They said I would be receiving the amount of two small Coke cans. I would get the first half over a fifteen-minute period. Once that was done, they would start the second syringe. They administered this through my PICC line.

We were all watching the procedure happening, but I couldn't feel anything. While I was receiving my transplant, I called Tanner on FaceTime so he could watch it happen. The cells did not look like blood exactly. It was a light color with a bit of white to it, like a fatty blood.

The specialist who was giving me my new cells said to my family, "Now Rebecca won't be able to notice, but she will smell like garlic for the next few days as the cells take over her body."

Sure enough, I didn't notice anything, but my mom sure did. She said she could smell me from the hallway. The nurses said they could, too. It was common for all new transplants patients to smell that way. Why? I do not know. It is just a weird side-effect.

JOURNAL ENTRY

Transplant Day

Good evening!

Today is Day 0 and I received my new cells this afternoon!!

My morning started out a little rough with some nausea and I got sick a few times. Around 9:00 AM I went down to the hyperbaric chamber. There are two chambers in the room. Someone was in the chamber next to me the whole time. Envision the tube deposit system at the bank. That is what the chamber looked like to me: a big, clear tube. I was in there for two hours and got to watch the movie "Happy Gilmore" followed by some ESPN.

Once I was in the chamber, my ears popped as if I was in an airplane. Then once I got to pressure, the popping went away. Other than that, I didn't feel any different than normal.

Once I returned to my room, I felt nauseous, which was still from the chemo and radiation. I ended up getting sick again, but I was able to take an hour-long nap before receiving my cells. When I woke up from my nap, I was happy to see that my door had been decorated! When it is someone's cell day, they get a sign on their door wishing them a happy cell day! My nurses and aides went above and beyond and put a GIANT (floor to ceiling) palm tree on my door with a sign that says, "Celling into Paradise!" Of course, it also says Woo Pig Sooie!

When I received my new cells, I felt like a new woman! I received four giant syringes full of cord blood over about a 25-minute period. While I was receiving my cord blood, my parents were in the room with me, and I was able to FaceTime with Tanner the whole time! My siblings and their spouses were in the waiting room. They took turns coming back to see me after the transplant was done. I love my family!

After I received the cells, they checked my vitals every fifteen minutes for an hour to monitor my blood pressure. Now that I have my transplant cells, we wait for my body to engraft the new cells and for them to grow and divide!

The next 28 days are crucial because this when my body is most susceptible to infection. I have to be very careful with what I touch, who comes to see me, and who I am around.

Again, it is VERY important that, if you are planning to come see me, call or text me to make sure it's a good time, because I can only have two people in my room at a time. You should shower and have on clean clothes if you're coming after school or work. You cannot come if you've been around anyone who has been sick in the last two weeks or if you are sick yourself. And you should have a flu shot!!

I believe that the good Lord is watching over me and is healing me! I know that my body will accept these new cells as they're supposed to without complications. I am a strong believer in the power of prayer so PLEASE continue to pray for me! Pray that my organs will stay healthy and strong, pray for my nausea to go away, pray for my appetite to stay where it is, and for me to be able to eat on my own. (They say throat soreness is common and people are usually on a soft/liquid diet, but they want you to eat on your own as much as possible because they want to avoid putting in a feeding tube). Pray for my body to accept this RED ROCK PALM POTION without complications, and please pray for my overall strength and health. I couldn't do any of this without you guys and I continually thank you all for your prayers and support!

BWB

Believe it. Achieve it.

Becca

DAY BY DAY, WEEK BY WEEK

AFTER THE TRANSPLANT, I WAS STILL
getting very sick. I started to develop more symptoms.
My throat was extremely sore. It was like having strep
throat, but one hundred times worse. When you don't
have an immune system, your symptoms are awful. You
have nothing to help fight it off. You are surviving on faith,
strength, and support.

The best way I explain the transplant is that they killed
Becca and brought me back to life with Red Rock Palm
Potion, my new cells. They were keeping me alive with
transfusions and meds that they thought would help the
side-effects. I was just a study, however, so nothing was
guaranteed.

With my throat being so sore and my lack of appetite from being so nauseous, my diet was little to nothing. I ate yogurt, oatmeal, chocolate milk, and hot tea with protein added to it all. My weight was dropping. I was down from 125 to 115. I don't think I had ever seen my weight so low. It has always been 125, ever since I started to weigh myself back in high school. I was at the point that I would try to put on as much clothing as I could before stepping on the scale, just to try to make myself weigh more. But there was no way to get around it. My doctors were watching my weight like a hawk. I was trying to eat and put on weight. I did not want to be put on a feeding tube.

About this time, I developed a cough, a dry hack, on top of getting sick and having a raw throat from the radiation. It made everything worse.

I was still walking and doing squats each and every day. There were only two days when I was not allowed out of bed because my resting heart rate was so high. I remember my nurse telling me I would feel like shit over the next week, but to remember that it was only temporary. It would go away as soon as my counts started to come up.

I remember I was no longer allowed to drink water because I had to much sodium in my system. I had to start drinking Gatorade. Normally, I only drink water. I have never been a fan of sports drinks or soda or juice. But I learned to love my G2. I had to get so many ounces in every day. Every move I made was monitored. Even how much I peed and pooped. There was zero privacy. I was constantly inspected from head to toe by so many different specialists.

JOURNAL ENTRY

On Track

Good evening,

Today is day three after the transplant . . . I am still getting sick at least once a day. I'm feeling good except for my throat. It's absolutely killing me. My dry hack is an all-day thing now. It doesn't help my sore throat one bit; in fact, it makes it hurt worse. This morning, when I saw the doctor, he told me I have Mucositis. This is common to get after my treatments.

The most important thing is that I eat on my OWN. It's never good if they have to put you on feeding tubes. As much pain as I'm in, I'm going to eat and drink all I can. I'm a fighter and I will never give up! No pain, no game!

I am completely on a liquid diet. Oatmeal, soups, and shakes are all I can eat. I am doing mouth washes constantly! I am using a magic mouth wash to numb my mouth. It helps a little bit but not for long. I can feel the sores starting to come in under my tongue.

With all that said, I'm still right on track. As much as this sucks and hurts, it's all expected. Today was Dr. Al's last day on rotation. He shook my hand before he left and said "I'm very proud of you Rebecca. Keep up the good work, you're doing great!"

Then, later this evening, Dr. Shune (who's the newest BMT doctor to the group) popped in my room just to come visit me! She asked if I was ready to kick butt, as she was boxing in the air, then giving me a high five. She told me how she's so excited for me and can't wait for me to get out of here and get back to Arkansas! She also told me how she was going to go on a run tonight and run a lap for me because she knows I can't wait to get outside to run again. I feel honored to have such support from my doctors. I am so blessed to have such amazing doctors who care about me and really get to know me for who I am. They truly are amazing people!

Please continue to pray for my overall health, my throat and mouth to not worsen, pray for my cough and nausea to go away, and most importantly pray for my body to engraft with my Red Rock Palm Potion quickly and for those counts to come up!!!

BWB

Believe it. Achieve it.

Becca

JOURNAL ENTRY

All Is Well

Good evening,

Today is a lot better than yesterday was. I think the switch of my meds really helped. I still got sick today after breakfast, but that was before the meds were changed. My diet consists of oatmeal, apple sauce, hot tea, and shakes. All of which have protein added to them. All through today I was able to nibble down a little bit of a baked potato! I want to keep my weight up. I believe it and I will achieve it!

Today's message from Joel Osteen really spoke to me. He said I need keep saying over and over in my head: ALL IS WELL. The good Lord is putting me through this pain only because the end result is going to be bigger and better than ever before! It really made me gear up again and get my mind right. I'm a fighter; I don't give in to pain. I know that the good Lord is healing me each and every day. I am well and healthy. This is only going to make me better off in the end!

Tomorrow I plan on walking twice as much and nibbling down more foods.

*Today my white count was .0! This is normal for my type of treatment.
My doctor told me not to be alarmed. Everything I'm experiencing
is all expected. They say all my side-effects will stay with me till my
counts begin to recover. I still have a way to go, but I know with power
of prayer, God will get me there faster than planed!*

ALL IS WELL. I believe it and I am achieving it!

*I could not thank you enough for all your support. Keep the prayers
pouring in! Please pray that I'll be able to eat on my own over the
next several weeks while my counts are low. Pray that all my organs
stay healthy and for my mouth sores to heal. Most importantly, pray
that my body engrafts quickly with Red Rock Palm Potion so I can get
better! We need those counts to come Up Up UP!!*

BWB

Believe it. Achieve it.

Becca

IT WAS AROUND DAY FIVE WHEN I started
to develop little blisters under the skin from radiation.
My hands and feet killed. I couldn't do anything with my
hands. I could no longer hold a fork, open a lid, and I could
hardly even wipe my own bottom. The blisters stayed

under my skin. They never burst open. They were little red blisters with a black dot on them. They were tiny, but they were all over my hands. My doctors sent in a specialist who made a special cream for me that I would use on my hands. I wore gloves over them and I called myself Michael Jackson to give it some humor. They later began to peel. I looked so tan from the radiation, but it all peeled off. It was the craziest thing ever.

WEATHERING
THE STORM

OVER THE NEXT WEEK, I BEGAN TO HIT
rock bottom. My hand sores were so bad my family had to
feed me. I developed an infection in my PICC line. They
had to pull my line and take lots of blood to cultures to
find out what the infection was and where it was coming
from. My resting heart rate was 150, my lungs were filling
up with so much fluid it was seeping through my rib cage.
My liver enzymes were off the chart high. I was still getting
sick twice a day. Still, I continued to keep my faith and
remain positive.

Because my resting heart rate was so high, they didn't want
me getting out of bed. One night they gave me a diuretic
to make me pee. I peed so much I lost fifteen pounds!
I was given x-ray after x-ray, checking my lungs and the
fluid buildup. The x-rays showed a spot on my lung that

wouldn't go away. The doctors were worried it was GVHD (Graft Versus Host Disease) in my lungs, which is a not a good sign. GVHD is the body trying to fight off the donor cells.

They called in a pulmonary specialist to examine me. They wanted to do a biopsy on my lung, but the specialist did not think it was necessary. The spot was small. He said they would do more damage if they biopsied it. Instead, they decided to wait and keep watching it. After that, the pulmonary specialist and his team would come and see me every day.

I was also seeing a heart doctor regularly. Because my resting heart rate was so high, they wanted to monitor it to make sure I didn't have a stroke or a heart attack. He put me on an oxygen tube to help with my breathing.

I had a fever at the time, so they had to pull my PICC line. I was seeing an infectious disease doctor and his team. I was peeing blood and I thought I was having my period, but it hurt so badly whenever I peed. Come to find out, I had the BK virus. They were able to put me on medications to help this issue, but it took about ten days to go away.

During this time, I was getting treatment under a tent to protect me from getting pneumonia. To top it all off, I developed C-Diff. I'd had it early on, too. It is extremely contagious to patients without an immune system. Once this was diagnosed, any nurse or doctor that came into my room had to completely gown up and put on a mask and gloves. It was kind of nice having them gown up. I felt like it was helping keeping the germs out of my room.

I know I am probably missing half the things that were going on in my body. At some point, your mind shuts off all the bad stuff and tries not to remember. My mom, on the other hand, who was my caretaker, could give you every detail and date when things happened. She was my drill Sergeant and got me through every day.

People ask me what I did every day. I spent half the day getting examined by different teams of doctors. I ran a fever for about seven days straight. It was very painful. I told my siblings I felt like I had strep throat. I was so out of it that week, I couldn't even find the strength to write on my blog, which I had updated every single day. My sister had to update it for me. Below are her posts during this time.

JOURNAL ENTRY

By Kristi Olson, 9/18/2014

Today is Day +9. Today has been another rough day for Becca. She ran a high fever all night last night and all day today. She is also having very bad shakes from her fever, which is making her body very tense. She hasn't slept much. Her heartrate has also been very high, due to trying to fight the fever off.

The good news is that her liver enzymes are down and are almost at a normal level. The doctor also said that the sonogram of her liver was good, and everything is functioning normal.

Since her central line was removed yesterday, they placed a new PICC line in her right arm today. The doctor also ordered a CT scan for her lungs. She has a hacking cough, and they just want to take every step they can to make sure it does not turn into anything else.

My amazing mom has been feeding Becca. Mom told me today that her friend Patti called her and asked if she had done the "airplane" into Becca's mouth. My mom told me she was going to do that at dinner to get a laugh out of Becca!

As hard as this may be to believe, Becca was told that she needed to get up and walk today. She got up and walked two laps. Even though she is exhausted and fatigued, she still pulled herself out of bed and walked.

In the midst of the storm, she is focusing on God and she's pulling all her strength from Him. The weak are made strong in the Savior's love! I love the song "Cornerstone" by Hillsong! If you have never heard it, I encourage you to listen to it, think about Becca, and the battle she is facing. Everyone is amazed by all the strength she has, but it is all from Him.

Please continue to pray for Becca. Pray for her fever, cough, and infection to subside. Pray for her strength, and for her fever to go away, and most importantly for her body to engraph.

BWB

Believe it. Achieve it.

Kristi

JOURNAL ENTRY

By Kristi Olson, 9/19/2014

Today is day +10 and it's been a crazy day! Becca still has a dry hacking cough, which had her up most of the night. She started the morning with a breathing treatment and a blood transfusion.

The doctor came in and told her that they saw some spots in the upper left quadrant of her lung from the CT scan and want to further investigate them. They called in a pulmonary specialist; he came in and evaluated Becca. They wanted to do a scope of her lungs and draw some fluid out to find out more what is going on. However, you cannot eat six hours before the procedure, and she had just eaten some peaches. He said that he felt she was on the tail end of whatever she has. They are going to wait until Monday, and if she still has her cough then they will do the procedure early in the morning.

They also sent in an infectious disease doctor. They called him in to make sure that she has all the right medications for the infections that she has. She has still been running a slight fever all day. Her pulse is also really high, and she has had some labored breathing.

However, she does feel a little bit better. She still has no energy to feed herself so my dad, my mom, and I all got to feed her today. She did get sick just a little bit ago for the first time in three days. She is pretty sure it is from all her coughing. They have her on some meds to help with the cough.

I was there today for three hours. During that time there was a total of four doctors, four nurses, two nurse practitioners, a nutritionist, an aide, and the cleaning crew. Mind you most of them came at different times.

Our mom forced her out of bed and made her walk two laps again today.

Becca's amazing friends at the Leukemia lymphoma society light up the night in honor of Becca!! Even if she does not respond to your texts or post she is having them read to her.

Thank you so much for all the love that you show to my sister!!!

Please continue to pray for her cough and infection to subside; for her breathing and her heart rate. Pray for her lungs to heal and her fever to go away. Please pray for her body to engraph and accept the transplant.

BWB

Believe it. Achieve it.

Kristi

I WAS AT MY ALL-TIME LOW. I wasn't sure if I was going to ever get better. My throat hurt so bad; my heart rate spiked anytime I got out of bed. By bottom area was so sore from an infection I was battling. I had to pee constantly from all the fluids they had me on. In spite of all of that I still showered every morning, put on my makeup and got dressed. I had no hair on my head, no eye brows or eyelashes. I was so yellow from being jaundice. My makeup was easy to put on, just a little eyeshadow.

One night my friend Theresa was staying with me. I was on so many fluids I woke up from a sound sleep and yelled to her, "OH MY GOSH, I HAVE TO PEE." She was across the room. Getting out of bed with cords all over that pull on you wasn't easy. Needless to say, I peed on the floor the whole way to the bathroom. We laughed so hard. I paged the nurse they had to have the cleaning team come in and mop my floors at 2AM. That night they brought a commode in and put it next to my bed.

I'll never forget one of my nurses came into my room one day and said she had a story she wanted to share with me. She said that this morning, when she woke up, she didn't want to get ready for work and starting complaining what the day was going to be like. Then she stopped herself and said, "I bet Rebecca isn't complaining and I bet she put her make up on this morning." She continued to share how she started to put on her makeup and was crying as she did it thinking about me when her daughter walked into the bathroom and asked her what was wrong. She said, "if Rebecca can do it I can to. This girl is fighting for her life." I felt so good that she told me this story, it was truly inspiring. I felt If I could do something so simple each day that could change someone's life, I was succeeding.

SUPPORT

AS EACH DAY GOT HARDER, MY SUPPORT
group grew stronger. My family and friends were by my
side the whole time. They made sure I knew I was not
in this battle alone. As I have said, I treated my illness
like a football season: I was the team, my doctors and
nurses were my coaches, and my family, friends, and even
strangers were my fans, cheering me on toward the big
WIN: Kicking Cancer's ASS!

The head coach at the University of Arkansas was amazing
to Tanner and let him come see me any chance he could
get. I will forever respect him for that. I was so encouraged
by everyone's comments on my Facebook page, the phone
calls and texts, and all my visitors. I can't remember the
lady's name or what church she was with, but she had
heard about me. She came to my room one day and asked

if she could pray with me. She blessed me with Holy oil on my forehead. After that, she came and visited me a few times a week. She didn't stay long, but she would ask how I was doing and dig deep into my spiritual roots and then prayed with me. Her visits brought my mother and me to tears. I felt like she was bringing me even closer to God.

One of my mom's friends told me that God only puts his strongest warriors through the toughest battles because he knows they can handle it. She said, "He will take you to your limits but never break you or give up on you. God wants to see how far you can go, and whether or not you will crack or give up on faith." I held on to that every day. I reminded myself I would be fine because I was putting all my faith, worries, and fear in God. I trusted in Him and believed He would make things better and I would be stronger after all of it. Whenever I began to worry or get nervous, I had a few songs I listened to that would help calm me and remind me that God was with me.

One amazing story during this time always brings tears to my eyes. My oldest niece, Olivia, who was three years old at the time, would call me on Face Time.

One day she said, "Aunt Becca, you're going to be fine." I laughed and smiled as she said it. She said, "I prayed to God last night, and He told me you're going to be ok."

I started to cry, and I had to hold the phone away from my face so she couldn't see me. I cried tears of pure happiness and astonishment. After I got it together, I came back to the phone and my sister was there, crying, too. I believe God was speaking to my niece, and that was His way of letting me know I would be ok. Whenever I would get scared and wonder how I would beat this, I would think of my little niece, Olivia, letting me know I was ok. I knew I was going to make it because she told me I was. I held on to that the whole time.

ROCK
BOTTOM

DAY 32: NOTHING WAS HAPPENING. STILL

no movement with my counts. Everyone was getting
frustrated, worried, and scared about what was going to
happen. The doctors were really starting to get worried.
They were beginning to talk about the next treatment
option: a Haplo, which is a half match with my oldest
brother Todd. Half of our DNA is in the exact same order.
My siblings and I all have the same DNA, but the numbers
had to be a perfect ten for a donor match. All of us were in
a different order. Todd was the closest match.

They brought my brother in for further testing. They
told him he would have to get 150 bone marrow biopsies.
They would put him under for it. I hated that for him.
I can't stand the pain of one, and he was getting 150?
He was pumped. He didn't care about the pain—he was

going to do whatever he could. He called me after one of his appointments, so excited. The nurse told him he had beautiful veins. I laughed. They said they had to put my brother under and get it from his actual marrow, because if they didn't, I wouldn't respond. They typically get the marrow from the arm, unless it's a critical situation. When I say they get it out of their arm, if you are a match for someone they would have you come in and donate your marrow you would sit in a chair and they would take blood out of one arm and a machine behind you would pull the marrow out and they put your blood back in your other arm. For more serious situations like mine they would have to take the marrow directly from your back. They use medical tools that cut through the skin and go deep into your hip bone and suck the marrow out of the bone. Its pretty painful but you are not put under for a normal biopsy they just numb the area. For my brother they were going to have to put him under for the amount of marrow they needed to get from him.

They decided to do another bone marrow biopsy on me, too, to see if there were any improvements. Just a couple days later they came in to let me know that I had 97% donor marrow, but the cells were very immature and might not be strong enough to grow.

Later that week, I remember one of the seven doctors
I see on weekly rotation, came into my room. He said
"Rebecca, we have to move forward. You're not responding
to your transplant. If we don't, you're going to get a serious
infection and die. You have had no immune system for 35
days now."

He began to tell me that I was going to have to go through
the exact same treatment regimen that I had just gone
through. We had a family meeting with the doctor. I told
him they could not do that to me again. They would kill
me if they gave me radiation and chemo again! I was not
strong enough to go through it. I was so mad, yelling at
him and telling him that plan was bullshit. I was not going
to do it!

He said "You have no other option. You will die."

I asked him how many people he had done this to. He said
he had done this procedure with only two others, and that
was years ago. I asked what their outcome was. He said
they died.

I said, "Then NO. I am not doing it."

After the doctors left the room, I called Tanner. I was bawling. I told him the bad news, that I would have to start over with everything. I told him I felt this would kill me. I couldn't do it! He started to bawl on the phone with me, we were crying together. He reassured me that it was going to be ok too.

My dad started to call other hospitals and asked my doctors to do the same. They did. They wanted to find out if anyone else had any cases like mine. They also performed another bone marrow biopsy on me only five days after the last one, to see if I had more donor cells maturing.

I was standing in my room updating my motivation word of the day. I said to my mom, I wonder if I made a mistake not picking Todd as my donor in the beginning. My mom said she had wondered that too. We were just so much alike.

While we waited to get my biopsy results, I was moving forward. I said, if I am going to have to get chemo and radiation again, then I need to start rehab and training. I had my doctor send up the physical therapist for leukemia patients. He came in and started to do leg and arm exercise with me. He told me I was strong and didn't really need his help. That gave me motivation. In my head, I was like

"You're right! I don't need you. I got this. I can do this! I can beat this cancer. I am not going to die; I have too much to live for." His encouragement put me back in the mindset that I needed. Every day, when I would walk the hall, there was a window that overlooked the parking garage. I liked going to the window and looking out while I did 25 squats.

At this point, I was willing to try anything and everything to get my counts up. My parents went to a Chinese doctor down the road. He gave them some dates, or maybe they were beans, that apparently help boost your white count. It was a fruit, but they had to be cooked. My mom went home and cooked them then put them in snack-size Ziplock bags and froze them. After that, my sister in-law, Katie, made me oatmeal with them. I ate them every night. I had the nurse bring them in at 11:00 PM every night.

I also started rubbing lemon oil on my hips, collarbone, and quads. I did that every night at 2:00 AM before they took my labs. I also did 25 squats and 50 jumping jacks whenever I put the oils on. I thought that if I got my heart rate up, that would get my blood flowing and maybe it would help my counts. I then started to request my labs to be drawn around 2:30 AM or later. I never wanted them to draw my labs too early. I wanted time to allow them to come up.

JOURNAL ENTRY

Day +32

Good evening,

Today is Day +32. My counts dropped again. My hemoglobin dropped as well, so I'm now receiving a unit of blood. My white count today is 0.1. I have some very important news and it's not the greatest. Although I'm 97% donor in my marrow and 88% donor blood, I only have a 5% donor blast, which they like to see 44%. They said I have ten more days to get my counts up! If my counts show no sign of recovery by day 42, I'll get another bone marrow biopsy. Then we'll have the family talk about the next step.

Please pray every second you get to bring my white count up!

I am not going to let this worry me. I'm trusting in the good Lord and the power of prayer. I BELIEVE we can do this together. They switched over some of my medications. I'm on two antibiotics treating a virus I have. They say this can make it harder for my counts to come up, but they should still be able to come up over the virus.

Today I have been feeling good. My mom and I have been watching college football, walking, and now we're flipping back and forth from the Razorbacks to the Royals game! I sure do love my sports!

Tonight, I'll get my blood drawn between 2 AM and 4 AM. Pray for God to BLESS MY BLOOD and BRING IT UP! This can't wait any longer. They need to see changes every day from now on, until day 42. If my counts come UP, we will not have to worry.

Please pray for my organs to stay healthy. Pray for my virus to subside. Pray that all the medications/antibiotics I'm on work for me. Most IMPORTANTLY, pray that God will bring my COUNTS UP.

BWB

Believe it. Achieve it.

Becca

JOURNAL ENTRY

Day +35

Today is Day +35. Last night I spiked a fever. They ran blood cultures on me, then put me back on the medication that they took me off last week. My bilirubin went up again last night. When the doctor came in today, he was concerned about it. My mom suggested taking me off the medication they had put me on last week. That's when my bilirubin started to go up again. They talked with the pharmacist and about what medicines could be affecting my liver counts. There were two that I was on that could be causing problems. One was the drug from last week the other is a pill I take to prevent pneumonia. They are stopping both of these today.

If my bilirubin counts don't go down in next couple days, they will do a biopsy. The doctor on call this week is going to recommend that they proceed with the next transplant. But they can't do that until they know what's going on with my liver. My eyes are yellow and my body is on fire because of my liver.

Today I received a breathing treatment for pneumonia. They came to my room and put me in this bubble and I had to breath into this machine for twenty minutes. It tasted so nasty!

We still have hope that we can surprise everyone, and my counts will recover!! I'm not giving up on my first transplant yet. Tomorrow, Todd goes in to get a series of tests done to make sure he's healthy enough to do the transplant. He's super pumped. "I'm a HAMMER, BECCA! I can't wait to save your life!!"

We won't know the details on plan B until the middle of this week. Regardless, I'm ready for whatever they have to do. I ask you to pray now that my bone marrow is NOT and will NOT be permanently damaged from all the chemo and radiation. This is my main concern.

My legs are extremely weak, and they shake all the time. I haven't been able to walk much, and I've been in my bed more than normal.

Please pray for my organs, my overall health, my bilirubin to go down. Also pray that my bone marrow is not permanently damaged. Pray for my counts to come up and surprise everyone!!!

BWB

Believe it. Achieve it.

Becca

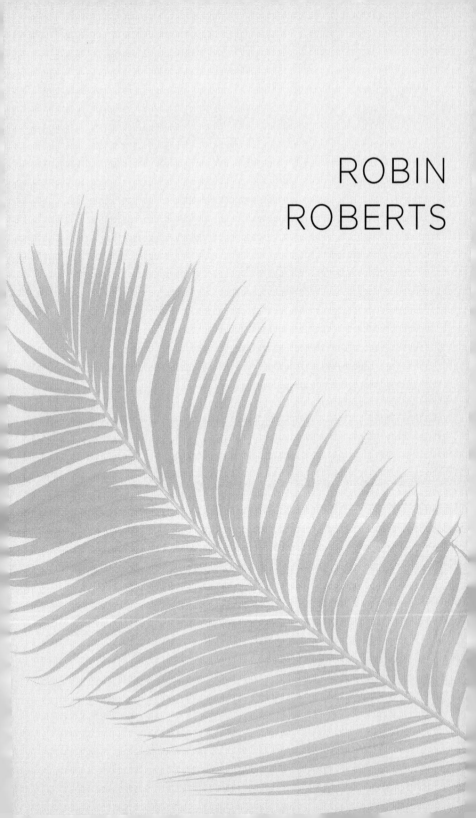

ROBIN
ROBERTS

IT WAS A PHONE CALL I WILL NEVER forget. My dad was staying with me that night at the hospital. He had just left the room to go get dinner from the hospital cafeteria. My phone rang: UNKNOWN NUMBER came across the screen. I contemplated not answering it. It was probably just a sales call. Finally I answered it.

"Hello?" I said in an annoyed tone of voice.

"Rebecca, this is Robin Roberts. How are you?"

My jaw dropped! I jumped up in my bed and changed my tone of voice.

"Oh my god, hey!!" I thought, no one is going to believe
me when I tell them Robin Roberts called me! I put her
on speaker phone grabbed my video camera and started
to record so I had it on film. We spoke for 13 minutes. I
tweeted after tagging her in the video and she retweeted
me. It was great getting that phone call from someone who
has been right where I was. She was an idol of mine.

My dad came back in the room and I said, "You will never
believe who just called me." He started to laugh. He didn't
believe me. Then I showed him the video. He was in
shock. I was like a schoolgirl on cloud nine! I was so happy,
smiling ear to ear. That was just what I needed to keep my
motivation going. After talking with Robin Roberts, I was
ready for the next fight in this battle. If I needed another
transplant, I was ready for it.

BLOOD
WORK

IT WAS THE DAY I WAS SUPPOSED TO
start chemo again. My labs showed that my liver enzymes
were off the chart. My doctors came in that morning and
told me I couldn't start chemo. I had to have a liver biopsy.
This was very dangerous. I could bleed to death due to no
white counts, or I could get an infection. I told them the
danger was too much and I did not want to get it done.
But, they said it had to happen.

Later they sent in the specialist who would do the biopsy.
He assured me it was not too bad. They would go in with
a scope through the main artery in my neck. The other
option was to cut me open and to go in through my gut.
However, because I did not have an immune system, it was
better to go in through my neck. That made me feel better.

I remember this was on a Thursday. My dad and brothers got word that the procedure was dangerous and my brother, Brian, called me.

"Bec are you ok? You feel ok, right? I heard you could die from this biopsy."

I said, "Shit, I feel great. I am not going to die. The doctor made it sound way worse than it is. The specialist who is going to be doing the procedure talked to me about it."

Brian was relieved. He asked if he needed to come to the hospital to be with me. I told him no, not to worry, and that I would be just fine. My mom walked me down to the room that evening where I was going to have the procedure done. When I came out of the biopsy, both of my parents were waiting. We had to wait for the results to see if I had GVHD, or possibly cancer in my liver. We had to wait for the culture to come back, which would take more than 24 hours, leading us into the weekend.

JOURNAL ENTRY

Good afternoon,

Today the doctor came in really early to tell me that they were going to go ahead with the liver biopsy. They don't know what's going on. My bilirubin level was still high today. They are pumping me with lots of platelets so that I will not bleed during the biopsy. They will go through an artery in my neck and down to my liver in order to do the biopsy. I will obviously be put under for this procedure, so please, please, PLEASE pray that there are no complications with the procedure and that we finally get some answers. I will go down in a couple of hours, so please pray as hard as you can.

All of the doctors here are very concerned for me because my counts have been low for so long. They say this is a very rare case and not something they are used to dealing with. They have been reaching out to other hospitals who have done double transplants when the first one didn't work. They are hoping some another doctor may have seen something like this and can help them figure out the best treatment option for me.

They are going to try and put a rush on the results from the biopsy today, but they aren't sure when they will get them back. They may go ahead and start me on chemo before they get the results because they don't think I can afford to wait any longer. I will do six days of chemo and one regimen of radiation. All of this is at a lower dose than the first round before transplant. Todd will begin Neupogen shots to increase his white blood cell count and they will draw the blood from his marrow on Friday and immediately deliver it to me for transplant. So, transplant day is next Friday.

I'm tired of being a rare case and my body not working like it should, I wish for once I could just be a normal case. I pray to God that my doctors can get some answers, and I hope you will too.

PLEASE pray for my procedure to go ok, for us to finally get some answers, for all of the doctors all over the country who will be helping my doctors . . . please pray that God will guide them in the right path and choose the best treatment for me, pray that Todd has no issues while he is prepping for the transplant, pray that my body will go through chemo and radiation with flying colors, and just please pray that this transplant will work.

BWB

Believe it. Achieve it.

Becca

JOURNAL ENTRY

Amazing Doctors

My doctors told me today that I am known all over the United States. They have been consulting doctors all over the US to figure out a plan of attack for me. I am so blessed to have such amazing doctors.

Dr. Al reviewed my bone marrow slides three times to make sure that they know everything, and Dr. Sing viewed them twice. Dr. McGurik is the doctor I am seeing this week. He said he was ready to pull the plug yesterday and start me on chemo to get me prepped for another transplant, but Dr. Al saw more growth in my myeloid cells than last time.

As a team, they have decided what is best for me is to wait and see if my counts come up. He did tell me that this will be a day-by-day decision, so we need my white counts to come up. Dr. McGurik told me he was praying for me constantly and wanted me to pull through this. He said he feels like he has aged ten years just watching me going through all of this. I agree, I think we all might have aged ten years.

BWB

Believe it. Achieve it.

Becca

PRIVATE
JET

MEANWHILE, THAT SATURDAY NIGHT,

Tanner arrived. The Razorbacks' head coach, Bret
Bielema, flew Tanner to Kansas City on a private jet to be
by my side. My life was on the line at this point.

The next day we got the results. There was no explanation
for what they found: my liver was normal! The doctor said
they would watch my counts carefully, but they planned to
start me on chemo on Monday.

That Sunday morning, my white count jumped for the first
time to 0.3. This was the first time it had jumped like that
since the transplant. Tanner joked that it was the power
of him being there. We will never know if it was it the
Chinese beans, the oils, the squats, the time they took the
labs, or simply a miracle from God. I believe it was God

putting his foot down and letting my doctors know that he had a plan for this transplant to work. The little boy's blood in me was going to be my new blood.

My doctor was in absolute shock when my count jumped. It was day 42 when my count started to climb. He said, "Rebecca I am going to give you a few more days and see if your count keeps coming up."

Sure enough, it did! I believe that my faith and never stop believing is what got me to this point.

JOURNAL ENTRY

Just in case I don't mention it enough, I am so blessed to be part of the Razorback family! Coach B is flying Tanner up on a private jet after the game today so that he can come see me. He will have to leave tomorrow morning, but I will take all the time I can get with him! This has been such an emotional week for us, and it will be amazing to have Tanner here, even if it is just for the night! Coach B will forever hold a special place in my heart, and I will always be a fan of his!

Today has been a good day. Mostly because there is not much to update about. Everything is the same as yesterday. Today, when Dr. McGuirk came in, he said they were seeing improvement, but they need to see more.

I had a nice surprise when Tanner got here this morning. I thought he had to leave today, but he doesn't have to leave till tomorrow! I was so excited when he told me that.

The whole time I have been in here, my unit has been under construction. Tomorrow they are opening up the other side of the unit! I will now be able to walk in a horseshoe instead of just a hall!

We are still patiently waiting for my white count to come up!

I could not be more blessed for my amazing support group. I would not be where I am today without all your prayers. I am also so grateful for the good Lord and all that He has blessed me with during my journey.

Please pray for my overall health. Most importantly pray that we see my white count jump UP UP UP!

BWB

Believe it. Achieve it.

Becca

COUNTS
COMING UP!

JOURNAL ENTRY

Today might be one of the best days ever! God is truly amazing and is answering all of our prayers. I could not praise Him more for all He has blessed me with.

My white count took a big jump and is at 0.7. We now know the transplant is working. My ANC is at 420, this has to be at 500 to go home. There is a good chance I could get there tomorrow, but Dr. McGuirk told me I'm not allowed to leave till my virus is completely cleared up. My virus is getting a lot better, but I'm still on antibiotics for it. He said the earliest I'll get to go home is at the end of the week!!!!

Today my mom and two of her friends, Cheri and Patti, went to my brother's house to deep clean it. They are getting his house ready for me.

I pulled another prank on Dr. McGuirk today. Whitney, one of my aids drew a face on the back of my head. When he walked in I had my back facing him, showing off my new face. He loved it so much he took a picture with me and sent it to the whole team.

Today, when Dr. McGuirk came in, he said "Rebecca you are going to be known worldwide. I'm going to share your case with everyone at our conventions."

Dr. McGuirk is also playing a little prank on Dr. Al tonight. At the beginning of the week Dr. McGuirk said that if this works, he's going to give Dr. Al kisses. Tonight, at their team meeting, he's going to call Dr. Al up and thank him for being so persistent about my case and then say "I owe you a kiss . . ." Then he'll grab Dr. Al and give him a bag of Hershey kisses!

Tonight, my mom and I are cheering on the Royals. I've been looking forward to this game all week!

Please pray for my virus to heal quickly and for my counts to continue to go UP UP UP!

BWB

Believe it. Achieve it.

Becca

NOW THAT MY COUNTS WERE COMING
up, I was able to leave the hospital. However, I couldn't
leave until I came off of my medications. They started
to taper me off the different medications, but it was a
challenge for me to stop using Fentanyl. I was using this
because I suffered from a serious infection on my bottom.
Anytime I went to the restroom, I would hit my pump
to help take the pain away. The pain was so bad I would
scream.

It was a huge struggle for me. I wanted to get out of the
hospital so much, but I was scared to go to the bathroom
without the pain meds. I think I was becoming addicted
to it. My mom and I would butt heads about this—she
would get so pissed if I used it. If it wasn't for her pushing
me, I don't know what I would have done. Finally, I slowly
started to taper off of it. My doctors said they could give
me Oxycodone to help with the pain as needed, but I didn't
want to take that unless I absolutely had to.

Weeks went by and I was finally able to come off the
Fentanyl. I still hated going to the bathroom. I was asked
every day if I'd had a bowel movement. If I said no, the
nurses would give me a stool softener. There were many
times I wanted to lie and say yes, just so I didn't have to go
to the bathroom and deal with the pain. My bottom was so

bad that I couldn't wear jeans or anything tight, only baggy pants. Even walking was extremely painful. The doctors said that once my counts were fully recovered it would go away.

On day 59 I was able to leave the hospital for the first time since August. It was October 28, 2014. Even though I was going home, my bottom was still not healed. My mom had to become my nurse. I will never forget that day, though. I was so excited to get out of the hospital and eat my mom's home cooked meals again.

JOURNAL ENTRY

Leaving KUMED

I GET TO GO HOME TODAY! God is amazing and miracles do happen! Never give up faith, trust, or hope. God works miracles every day. I'll never stop believing. My white count took a huge jump overnight. I'm so blessed to have such amazing prayer warriors fighting this fight with me.

I have been in the hospital for a total of 59 days! So, so crazy. I'm not going to miss the hospital, but I am going to miss all my amazing nurses. It's so hard saying goodbye to them. They have become my family. If it wasn't for their amazing care, I wouldn't be where I am today. I truly love every one of them.

Today I am celebrating by ripping down my palm tree on my door. I did it! We did it! I am now Red Rock Palm Potion!

Just because I'm going home, doesn't mean my journey is over. I'm day +49 out from my transplant. The transplant isn't considered completely engrafted until day 100. I'm halfway there! I will be going to the cancer center every day for the first week or so, starting tomorrow.

The rules are the same at home as they are in the hospital. I'm not allowed to go outside until day 100. Whenever I'm out of the house, I have to wear a mask.

Anyone is welcome to come visit me at my brother's house, but these are the rules:

Recommend you have the flu shot

No children under age 12 are allowed to be around me.

You MUST shower and be in clean clothes before coming to visit me.

You're not allowed to visit if you've been sick or if you've been around someone else who has been sick. You must wait two weeks after your symptoms are over, or after you've been around that person.

Still no hugging me or touching me.

My mom and I are moving into Brian and Katie's house. We have to be within thirty miles of the cancer center. I'm so grateful they are opening their doors up for me to stay with them. It's going to be a lot of fun. I have to have a caretaker 24/7, in case something happens. My amazing mother will be by my side. I'm so grateful to have her.

I'm still at the hospital. I won't be discharged till around 4 PM. It still hasn't hit me yet. I really can't believe I'm going HOME! Today will be the first time in 59 days that I've walked up stairs. That's going to feel so weird.

I had an amazing visit today from Andy Reid's wife and a couple of the Kansas City Chiefs' coaches' wives. They could not have been more fun. I had a blast visiting with them. They also gave me a signed football from Andy Reid, a shirt, and a hat. I can't wait to rock it for next week's game!

Also, some more exciting news: A friend of mine who joined the bone marrow registry at one of my drives received a letter in the mail yesterday that she is a match for someone! They would like her to come in for more testing. I am so happy that there's a chance she could save someone's life!

I could not THANK YOU ALL ENOUGH for all your prayers and support. Please never stop! I will update you tomorrow with more details on my appointments and the next steps from here. We still aren't sure what time my appointment is tomorrow at the cancer center, but I'll post as soon as I get out of there.

AHHH! I GET TO GO HOME!!!!

BRIAN'S
HOUSE

SINCE MY PARENTS LIVE MORE THAN
35 minutes away from the hospital, I couldn't go to their
house when I was discharged. I had to be closer. We were
offered the Hope House, or I could stay at my brother
Brian's house, since he lived closer to the hospital. All of
my siblings lived within 35 minutes of the hospital, but
Brian was the only one without kids.

They did have a dog, and my doctor said they had to
get rid of it while I stayed there. My sister-in-law was
devastated; that dog was her baby. At the time, my brother
and Katie were newly engaged and in their first house
together. I was the one crashing it—and now they had to
get rid of their dog? Still, they welcomed my mom and me
with open arms.

They had to make so many adjustments for me to be able to live there. In the end, I was able to convince my doctor to let them keep their dog. As long as he didn't sleep with me, or lick or cuddle with me, it would be ok.

Brian and Katie dedicated the basement to me. It was fully furnished and had a small kitchen. There was only one bedroom, though, so my mom slept on the couch outside my room. I struggled to sleep in the bed. It was amazingly comfortable, but I felt like I was having drainage issues whenever I laid flat. I had always kept my bed at the hospital elevated. So, I started sleeping on the recliner. My mom was on the big couch and I was on the recliner, and there was the bed, wide open!

I loved being around Brian and Katie. It made me feel somewhat normal. I always had my buddies with me. I am forever grateful for Katie: newly engaged, recently moved into a new house, and BOOM! We moved in and her whole life changed. I have a great sister-in-law. She did a lot for me during that time.

Because I was still suffering from my bottom issues, my mom had to give me my meds every day. I still had my PICC line and Home Health gave us everything we needed. My mom had to hook me up and administer my meds through my PICC line, then give me fluids

afterwards. I was also receiving a Neupogen shot twice a
day. My mom was not the best at giving me shots—she
would freak out—so Brian gave me my shots.

After about a month, my mom and I decided we could
move out to the farm—my parents' house was almost
an hour from the hospital. We moved out there without
telling my doctors. We figured that if something was
wrong, we could get in the car, call the hospital, and by the
time we arrived, they would just have a bed ready for me.
Finally, though, we had to tell them and they were ok with
it, so long as I could get to the hospital within an hour.

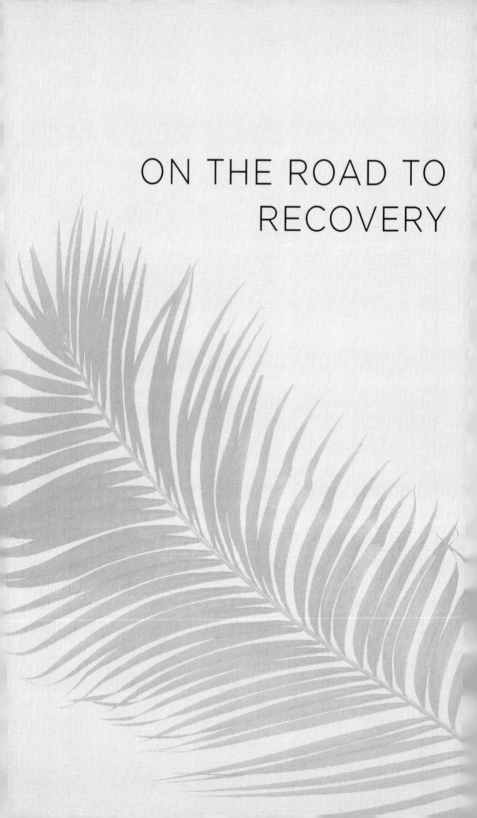

ON THE ROAD TO RECOVERY

I WAS GOING TO THE CANCER CENTER

almost every day. My mom was my personal driver. She took me to every single appointment. I will never forget the day we were running late to one of my appointments at the cancer center. My mom got pulled over. I was sitting in the front seat.

The police officer said "Ma'am, do you realize you were speeding? I need to see your licenses and registration."

She said, "I'm sorry. I am taking my daughter to her appointment." I leaned forward to wave at him. I was bald and wearing a mask—doctors' orders.

He gave her ID back to her quickly and said, "Go! Have a great day but get out of here! Take her to her appointment!" He walked away and we started to crack up.

My counts continued to recover as we waited to get to day 100 when they would do the next bone marrow biopsy. I had to live like I did in the hospital until I got to day 100. I wasn't able to hang out with friends or see my nieces and nephews. I had to live like my brother's house and the farm were still the hospital. My family and I were very strict on these rules. This was my life and my health; we needed to keep me healthy no excuses.

JOURNAL ENTRY

Cancer Center

Yesterday I saw Dr. Al. We had such a great visit and he told me that after day 100, I'm FREE! (To an extent.) he told me I could go without a mask, unless I'm around a large crowd. He also told me he didn't see a problem with me eating out again. I just have to carefully judge the foods I eat, and absolutely no buffets.

He also told me I could see all my nieces and nephews on Christmas Eve when we do Christmas with the family. He said I had to wear a mask though, wash my hands often, and shower after they left.

I told him he saved my life, and he said, no Rebecca you saved your life. He told me how much he admired me for my attitude and how it will get me a long way in life.

He spent thirty minutes with me, visiting and explaining my labs and their recovery. He said he had followed me very closely throughout my journey.

Yesterday wasn't my best day. I woke up with diarrhea and finished my night throwing up. I felt fine during the day, so I'm not sure what that was all about. Dr. Al said I could be showing signs of GVHD, which isn't bad. I also have a little rash on my obliques. It could just be dry skin, but if I keep having these symptoms, then it's most likely GVHD. They would just give me a steroid to help it.

Yesterday my creatine level was 1.55 which is pretty high. Home Health brought out a liter of fluid for me. Right now, my mom and I are heading back to the cancer center to get my levels checked. Once we get these results, we will know how to adjust my IV antibiotic. Some great news: Dr. Al took me off about half my pills! I went from taking twelve morning pills to only four pills! It's awesome!!

Tomorrow I come in at 9:15 AM for my labs, then my bone marrow biopsy is at 10 AM. They said they know I'm 100% donor, the main thing they will be looking for is to make sure I'm Leukemia free. I know the good Lord has healed me and has cured me from cancer.

Please pray for my overall health and wellness, pray that I remain cancer free and will always remain cancer free.

BWB

Believe it. Achieve it.

Becca

JOURNAL ENTRY

Bowl Game

Good morning,

We're going to the Bowl! I am so PUMPED! Arkansas not only won last night, they whooped Ole Miss! The Razorbacks have won six games this season, so they get a bowl game. Meaning, I'll get to go to a game this season and watch Tanner coach! That's all I have wanted to do all season. When I was diagnosed back in July, my main concern was not being there this season for Tanner. Now I finally get to go! The good Lord has blessed me with this opportunity.

Over the weekend Kali, Kels, and Theresa all came over and we baked cookies together. They were darn good cookies!

Saturday was just my mom and me. My dad and brothers went to Arkansas for the game. They had a blast—they picked a good game to go to.

Right now, mom and I are on the way to the cancer center. I have to get my levels checked for one of the medications that I'm on. I don't have to wait for these labs, so I'm literally going in to get blood drawn and then leaving.

Tomorrow I have labs and a doctor's visit.

I'm not sure why, but I'm getting nervous for my Day 100 bone marrow biopsy. I don't know why. I know the good Lord has healed me and has killed my marrow off and blessed me with another person's marrow. It's just always scary. I believe I'll be cancer-free from all cancers for the rest of my life.

The other day I was thinking how cool it would be to be on the Ellen show to share my story! I love her show—I watch it daily.

I'll update y'all tomorrow after my appointment.

Please pray for my overall health, pray that I keep getting stronger and get all my energy back! Pray for my infection to continue to heal.

BWB

Believe it. Achieve it.

Becca

JOURNAL ENTRY

Day 100 Results

I received fabulous news today . . . I'm Leukemia FREE! I didn't think I would have these results back yet. This morning when I saw Dr. Al, he told me they would find out today and they would call me with the news. Seeing their number come across my phone I think my heart skipped a beat. Lisa, the nurse practitioner, told me the great news. I've never done a bigger fist pump! As soon as she told me, I called all my siblings. Today I can finally say I'm a two-time CHAMPION!

Today I also found out that I no longer carry the gene inversion 16. This is the chromosome that carried the leukemia. And the best news of all: I'm 100% DONOR!

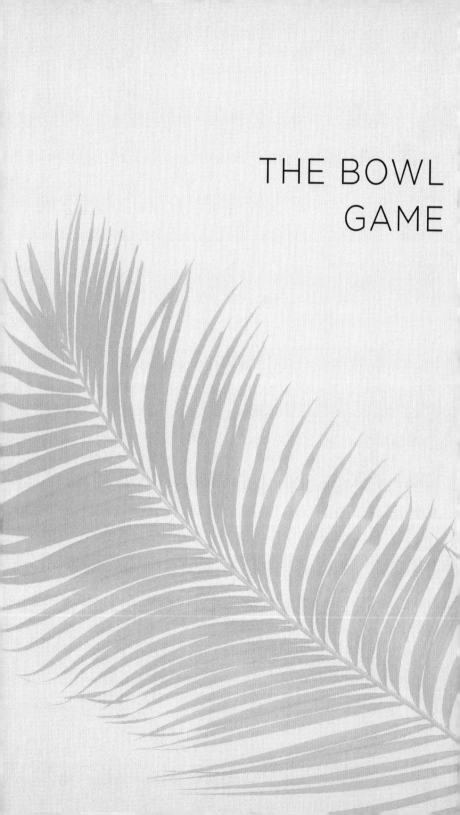

THE BOWL
GAME

I WAS 110 DAYS OUT FROM THE

transplant. I was suffering from bad diarrhea and still had
the issues with my bottom. Tanner's football team had
made it to the bowl game. I begged my doctors to let me
go. I think they allowed me to go as a get out of jail card. I
told my doctor you can let me fly on the plane that is team-
only, or my mom can drive me, and we will stop at nasty
gas stations and eat fast food.

He said, "Ok, ok, you can fly with the team!"

I was so excited. The team would fly out on Christmas
day. I was supposed to drive myself down to Arkansas
on Christmas Eve to spend the day with Tanner, but my
stomach was hurting so bad and I was so nauseous, I was
not sure if I was going to be able to go. The doctors gave

me an oil to take that was supposed to coat my stomach. It
was absolutely disgusting. It literally tasted like cooking oil.
I was taking that and Zofran to help get me through the
day.

I made it to Arkansas, however, and Tanner took me
out that evening to go walk around the square. It was all
decorated for Christmas. It was beautiful. He had our
apartment spotless and made me a nice homemade meal. It
was so sweet! I loved being with him and the little things,
like holding his hand and looking up at him. Hugging
meant the world to me. This life was almost taken from
me. We both knew it.

The next day we flew out to the Bowl Game in Houston,
Texas. It was so nice to be going to the game. I got to see
my coworkers and my football family. I spent most of the
time in the bedroom sleeping and getting sick, but I didn't
care. I felt blessed just to be there.

My doctors told me I was allowed to eat out just one or
two times during the time I was away. Tanner's college
roommate lived in Houston, so we went to dinner with
him one night. I also got to attend some of the Bowl
festivities.

My hair was starting to come back at this point, but it was very new. I still looked like I was sick. I wasn't able to style it at all; it was still too short for that. I also had to wear my mask everywhere I went: doctors' orders.

The Razorbacks won the game, and it was truly amazing! After the game we got to go out on the field and celebrate. Tears of joy rolled down my face. Not because we won, but because I was able to be there for Tanner. I was so excited I was able to attend one football game of the season—and what a game!

GVHD

WHEN I ARRIVED HOME FROM THE GAME,
I felt awful. The next day was New Year's Day. I was
getting sick out of both ends. My mom decided we were
going to the hospital. I had C-diff again, and on top of that
I had GVHD of the gut. GVHD is your body fighting off
the donor cells. GVHD of the gut meant diarrhea for days.

I was admitted into the hospital the next day. They
did lower and upper GI tests on me. That's when they
detected I had Stage 2 GVHD of the gut. I was placed
on Prednisone. I will forever have a love/hate relationship
with this drug. It cured my GVHD over the next few
months, but I blew up like a basketball! Because I was on
such a high dosage, my face got round, my belly looked like
I was pregnant, and I had a humpback.

When I was checked into the hospital, I weighed 97 pounds. WHAT?! I was like, no that can't be right. They told me they were treating me as an anorexia patient. I believe that's another reason why I was on such a high dosage of Prednisone.

Once again, I was suffering from my bottom issues. This time, they would not let me leave the hospital till they could get that infection healed. They tested different antibiotics on me until they found one that helped. After ten days in the hospital, I was able to check out. My mom was going to be my nurse again. The Home Health group shipped the IV medications and a pole to my parents' house. I was on this medication for a while.

Meanwhile I was gaining weight just fine from the Prednisone. I went from 97 pounds to 120 in a week! Finally, after two months of Prednisone, one of my doctors asked if my face hurt, because it was so round. He decided they needed to taper me off the steroid fast. That was music to my ears! My face took the longest to slim down. I think it took two years! To this day, I think it is rounder than it ever was before due to that dang Prednisone.

BELIEVED IT.
ACHIEVED IT!

I WAS SIX MONTHS OUT FROM
transplant and due for another bone marrow biopsy.
This was a big stepping stone. It would let me know if I
remained in remission and what percentage I was of the
donor marrow. I don't have patience when it comes to
results. My nerves were high while I waited those few days
to find out if I was still in remission. It would take a full
ten days to know the rest of my results.

I remember asking the doctor if he could let me know
within 24 hours. I knew this was possible. He had the
pathologist look at my bone marrow slides right away.
Their conclusion: I was in REMISSION!

I was so excited, I had tears of joy! God had blessed me. I
believe I have the blood of Jesus running through my veins

now. I believe I will never have to go through anything like this ever again. God took me to my limits and is using me as a testimony to others.

JOURNAL ENTRY

I'm officially a boy! Yesterday we saw Dr. Abyankar. He said, "Congratulations Mom, you have a baby boy!"

My XY chromosomes are 99.8% male and 0.2% female! Don't worry, I'm not going to turn into a boy. The only thing that changes is my chromosomes. It's so amazing how they can do that.

I called my dad and said, "Well Dad, I'm a boy!"

He was like, "WHAT!?"

We all got a great laugh about it, but I'm proud to be a boy, blood-wise. If it wasn't for that little boy's cord blood—my Red Rock Palm Potion—and God's amazing power, I wouldn't be here today.

Not a day goes by that I don't look back at all that I went through and my support group. I was really numb to it then, but now I'm rolling through the emotions and asking my loved ones: how did you guys stay so strong for me? How did we do that? Then I know: we all held on to our faith by the power of the good Lord.

I'm blessed every day in this amazing life and by all the loved ones around me and my support group. We all BELIEVED IT and we all ACHIEVED IT!

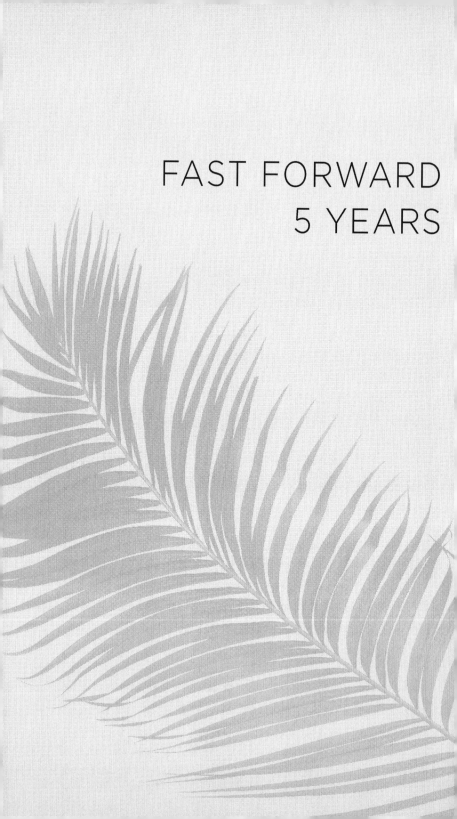

FAST FORWARD
5 YEARS

FIVE YEARS HAVE PASSED SINCE I
received the new that I my cancer had returned. This is
HUGE, I did it, I officially beat cancer and can put this
chapter of my life behind me. This just isn't 5 years it's 10
years later that I get to say I am CANCER FREE!!!!

On July 8, 2019 I had my five year follow up appointment.
They said since I was so far out I did not have to get a bone
marrow biopsy that I can do it all by labs blood from the
arm. I told them I wanted it from my marrow. They said
ok, if you insist, but that is not necessary. After I found out
how much I would have to pay after insurance I decided
to just get it drawn from my arm. Cancer doesn't just
mess with your body it messes with your mind. Months
before and the weeks leading up to my appointment I was
so nervous and anxious. I knew I felt fine but it's always

going to mess with my mind. Thankfully I have my mom, Tanner, sister and girlfriends that I can fall back on to express my worries. They all help me relax and give me such positive feedback to get my mind off the worst. Of course, I am always praying to go and praising him for all he has done for me and praying for my future health. Over the past five years the good Lord has blessed me in so many ways. I am now a wife to Tanner we got married in July of 2016. And I beat the odds again I a mother on October 2018 I gave birth to our beautiful baby girl who brings so much joy and happiness to our lives. It wasn't easy trying to get pregnant I spent countless months and days making trips to the fertility center after several months of trial and error in January 2018 we were able to get my body exactly how they needed it to implant our embryo. After one time implanting it took and now we have our baby girl. I am so blessed that I get to spend each and every day with her. We are no longer with the Arkansas Razorbacks but Arkansas will forever hold a special place in all of our hearts. I am so beyond thrilled to say this, I AM CANCER FREE!

NOTES FROM BECCA'S
DOCTORS AND NURSES

BECCA HAD THE CLOSET in her room full
of regular, every day, 24-year-old girl clothes; and she
got dressed every morning, as though she wasn't in the
hospital. She had a "look good, feel good" mentality, and it
was inspiring to witness.

Becca and I developed more than a nurse-patient
relationship. She became my dear friend. I remember
admitting her to the hospital when she was diagnosed, and
looking at the admission slip at her date of birth. Two and
a half weeks older than me. I stared at the date in shock, in
fear, and in heartbreak. I had cared for many patients older
and younger than me in my career, but never my exact age.
It hit me hard. I understood exactly where she was in life.
Her case taught me a level of empathy which I had never
experienced, and one that I was able to carry into all of my
patient interactions.

Love you, lady!!

—Crissy Kus, BSN, *RN*

Becca was a very courageous, determined, and positive person. She always believed that she was going to be healed of her cancer.

Becca's journey to sustained remission and possible cure from leukemia was complicated. The first few weeks after her transplant with no appreciable recovery of her blood counts was a nerve-racking experience. Despite the gravity of the situation, Becca was calm and collected. She knew, more than anyone, that she was on the right track and that she was in the process of being healed. Literature suggests that less than 5% of patients who do not recover their blood counts by day +42 after cord blood transplant end up recovering, which is a small chance. Despite that small chance, she always believed that she healing and recovering before we saw clear signs of her recovery.

Becca approached her treatment with confidence in her team and in her ability to get through treatment. She was always positive about her outcome and always believed in her ability to get through tough times. She always relied on her family and friends support and encouragement.

I still remember my visit with Becca when her leukemia came back. We discussed our treatment strategy. We discussed using umbilical cord blood for her transplant and our hyperbaric oxygen therapy study. She impressed me with her determination and her assertiveness. She was clear about her decision. Few moments after my visit, I saw her walking the halls with her family and friends following her. That moment made me feel that Becca was a very special person to her family

—Omar Aljitawi, MD (Dr. Al)

REBECCA HAS "THE EYE OF THE TIGER."

She was in harm's way with no immune system whatsoever, and I was very worried we would lose her, but she wasn't. She's my boss, so, when she wanted to be patient and give it more day, I followed her wishes. The next day showed a tiny white blood cell count. Rebecca has the determination to sit tight, and sure enough, the next day showed a few more white blood cells. Since then, her new immune system has grown beautifully.

—Dr. McGuirk

IT WAS VERY CLEAR TO ME after our initial interactions that behind the infectious child-like smile, you were mature beyond your age. vulnerable but vivacious all the time. It is never easy to spend your young years living under the dark clouds of a cancer diagnosis, but I was always impressed by your strong will especially when things were not going in the right direction.

Acute Myeloid leukemia is one of the most aggressive cancers, almost a death sentence when it relapses after an initial treatment. A stem cell transplant can provide cure to many patients, but many do not have well matched donors. Umbilical Cord blood transplant (UCBT) can allow many of the patients to undergo a life-saving transplant. However, there are so many ways this transplant can go wrong, rejection of the new stem cells, bad infections resulting from an underdeveloped immune system, just to name a few. You had all of these complications, but your strong will and family support managed to get you through these.

I try to learn something from every patient encounter and your case helped me develop a new respect for "uncertainty" in medicine. There are so many times in medicine when things are not going right and as a physician you want to "do" something to fix the problem because "doing" is hard-wired into our thinking. However, sometimes the best action is to pause and reflect. A better understanding of uncertainty helped me improve my clinical decision-making.

I am truly privileged to be one of your treating physicians and take great pride to be a part of your journey.

—Dr. Singh

Made in the USA
Middletown, DE
21 May 2020